The **New** Lion Economy

Unlocking the value of lions and their landscapes

Contents

1. Introducing the new lion economy

"Ultimately conservation is about people. If you don't have sustainable development around these (wildlife) parks, then the people will have no interest in them, and the parks will not survive."

Nelson Mandela[1]

Foreword

The lion – one of the world's most iconic animal species – is facing a catastrophic decline, with Africa's population dropping 50% in only twenty years. Lions will not survive the 21st century on goodwill alone. Nor will they survive if reduced to being merely the centrepiece of a high status vacation for foreign visitors to the continent, or even the target of trophy hunters.

Lion survival depends on Africa itself. This means drawing on the huge cultural value that lions have in African society to build consensus about the importance of their survival in the wild. More pragmatically, it depends on people, governments and industry recognising that concern about lion survival is not just harking back to a romanticised past, but symbolic of a whole range of other values that are at risk of disappearing along with the lion.

It is exciting, as an African, living at a time when the continent is changing in fundamental ways – finance, industry and politics are converging to create an opportunity for transformative change. But the Africa of 2030 is being crafted today solely on socio-economic development aspirations. In my travels across the continent and discussions with presidents, lawmakers, the youth, investors and other opinion leaders, I have come to learn that many leaders see destruction of the environment and wildlife crime as an existential threat. But this does not mean that they relate it to their national economic ambitions. The role that Africa's unique natural assets – wildlife and wildlands – will play in modern Africa are completely left out of the discussion.

Despite Africa growing fast, economically, culturally and in the confidence of its mainly young citizens, the continent will continue to be reliant on the range of ecosystem services provided by its wildlife, forests, savannahs and freshwaters: providing ecosystem services like clean water, buffering against floods and desertification, carbon storage, wild food and many more. Wildlife like the lions are indicators of many of these ecosystem services. A healthy lion population indicates healthy savannah and miombo, which in turn indicates vital contributions to food and water security, disaster risk reduction and climate stabilisation. Investing in lion conservation is not simply a charitable act that might protect populations of one particularly species, however important. It also protects the many commercial and subsistence values that rely on lions directly, or that rely on the landscapes where lions live, and come as a no-cost extra to conservation.

This report shows that the economic development of Africa and conservation of nature are convergent not conflicting goals. It is a false dilemma to suppose that Africa's wildlife and wild landscapes must or should be sacrificed in order for the continent to modernize and maintain

© AWF

Lion survival depends on Africa itself. This means drawing on the huge cultural value that lions have in African society to build consensus about the importance of their survival in the wild.

> The challenge is how do we line up all the development goal blueprints and marshal the various interests they represent in a way that ensures wildlife, like lions, have a future in modern Africa?

the steady pace of its economic growth. The challenge is how do we line up all the development goal blueprints and marshal the various interests they represent in a way that ensures wildlife, like lions, have a future in modern Africa? It is a question conservation groups like mine have been asking but the way forward must come from a multitude of stakeholders – governments, industry leaders, the private sector and civil society, all working alongside conservation and environmental groups.

Development and the protection of our ecosystems need not be mutually exclusive. Without stopping the pace of development, we must make better choices to minimize the consequences and net impact on nature's ecosystems. All of these things demand galvanizing political will to take action and now is the time to reflect about various costs – social, environmental and human, and to think about what's going to happen when our most precious assets and resources are depleted. If we want to change this, we all have to work together.

I am happy to welcome this report, the first to look in detail at the wider ecosystem services from lion landscapes. I urge everyone, and particular young Africans – you are the majority, this is your future; as part of the process of building your stake and getting to the helm of what is becoming the most important national asset – back the survival of lions and in doing so help back a sustainable future for yourself and for our great continent.

Kaddu Kiwe Sebunya,
Chief Executive Officer, African Wildlife Foundation

© Peter Lindsey

Preface

"Just as a private sector investor will not invest in something without knowing its likely returns, the Government must also know the value of nature, who is benefiting from it as well as the type of returns it is generating. This is vital to inform our planning and budgeting processes."

Pohamba Shifeta, Minister of Environment and Tourism, MP, Namibia[2]

The lion has become symbolic of the rapid economic growth experienced by some African countries. Labelled the 'lion economies' by policy makers and the press, commentators have had fun with wordplay related to 'lions', 'prides' and 'roars'.[3,4] But despite the iconic place that the lion holds in African society, and the conscious linking of economic development with the power of lions, there has been little notice taken of the risks that this development agenda brings for the lion itself.

Reversing the dramatic decline of wild lions in Africa has rightly focused on policy and legislation, habitat and prey conservation, management (e.g. fencing),[5] coexistence (mitigating the human costs of living with lions) and protection to combat poaching and retaliatory killing. But what if we fail – if we lose lions, what else might we be losing? Or put another way, if we protect what is left and restore the once extensive lion range across Africa, what else could we gain?

Lions are the ultimate 'indicator species' of healthy intact savannah landscapes in Africa.[6] Their dramatic decline is a sign of the pressures on land and communities throughout their range.[7] They are, or should be, at the top of the hierarchy of African animals; the predators which sit at the head of the food chain and help shape the vast landscapes that they inhabit. But in many areas, ecosystems are being degraded and lions are increasingly surviving only in small populations in highly protected reserves. These reserves require considerable management, including sometimes population control through killing and contraception, and thus only make limited contributions to ecosystem functionality and wider conservation outcomes.[8]

Unfortunately, there is surprisingly little recognition of the many benefits to humans from predators and scavengers[9] or from the landscapes they live in. An understanding that natural ecosystems are not just wasted space, but provide services of concrete and irreplaceable value to a modern society, is a critical step in tipping the balance back in favour of lions and other wild species.

We argue for a 'new' type of 'lion economy' that should be focused on **investment in the management of areas with wildlife to maintain ecosystem services and ensure that the latter play a key role in national sustainable development strategies**

© Egil Dröge

Overall, we hope this report makes the case for both lion conservation and the conservation and restoration of the lion range

As conservationists we need to plan, govern and incentivise our actions effectively. The focus of this report is on the last of these actions, providing effective incentives for lion conservation and an overview of the cumulative, often overlooked, benefits associated with the landscapes that lions inhabit across Africa. Relentless pressure for land use change is challenging traditional models of protection and conservation. But the more we remove or degrade natural ecosystems, the more we are likely to lose in terms of both ecosystem services and the associated economic and social benefits that they bring.

This report provides evidence that lions are a perfect flagship or umbrella species on which to focus policy and development decisions. Investing in lion conservation confers a range of benefits which are outlined in the following pages.

Executive summary

Lion conservation conserves much more than just lions

Africa's ecosystems generate goods and services that help secure the livelihood of over 62% of the rural population, more than 300 million people in sub-Saharan Africa, as well as supplying essential services such as water for its rapidly growing cities. **Landscapes supporting lions, "lionscapes", provide more ecosystem services, the benefits that humans receive from healthy ecosystems, than the average across Africa.** Yet many of these services will disappear if ecosystems are lost or degraded. Lions therefore make excellent indicators of ecosystem services and sustainable development. The Lion Recovery Fund has supported this report, the first of its kind, to highlight the importance of lions and their territories for Africans. **The New Lion Economy** shows:

Lions *directly support* ecosystem services: Iconic animals like lions attract tourists and trophy hunters worth millions of dollars every year to the economies of many African countries.

Lion conservation supports *other* ecosystem services: Even more significantly, lionscapes maintain many other services such as water sources vital for drinking water and power; store carbon to mitigate climate change; support food security; and protect communities against some weather-related disasters.

Lions also have important livelihood, cultural and political values: Lions are at the heart of African culture; recognising and managing for the wider values of lion conservation helps to build community and political support for co-existence.

Lions can generate economic benefits and attract new sources of revenue: Better understanding of ecosystem services from lionscapes will help gain access to different funding streams, which can support livelihoods and sustainable development as well as lions.

Lion conservation is not just a matter for conservationists, but for anyone interested in a sustainable and vibrant future for Africa. Lion populations are collapsing and have already gone from many countries. In a drive to build economies and lift people out of poverty, governments are reluctant to spend more money on conservation, seeing this as a diversion from other pressing needs. But they are ignoring the serious environmental problems being faced by the continent. Africa is already experiencing the loss of ecosystem services; and even more worrying, most countries have little resilience to climate change.

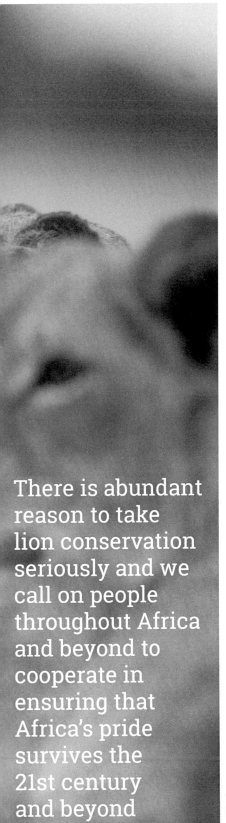

There is abundant reason to take lion conservation seriously and we call on people throughout Africa and beyond to cooperate in ensuring that Africa's pride survives the 21st century and beyond

© Brent Stapelkamp

Understanding the interconnectedness of land and associated flora and fauna, the way it is used and the services it provides are essential to establishing an equitable and sustainable future. Many conservation initiatives are protecting intact ecosystems, symbolised by the top predators such as lions, and promoting sustainable livelihoods. The map [overleaf] captures just a few of these initiatives within the lion range that are highlighted in this report.

Lion conservation needs serious investment if these wider values are to be retained

The 'new' lion economy is one in which investment is made into the management of areas with wildlife to maintain ecosystem services to ensure that these areas contribute to national sustainable development strategies. This new economy also links conservation management with ecosystem services, opening the door to a great range and diversity of funding options; such as payments for ecosystem services and the 'offset markets' where the 'polluter' pays for the negative impact they impose on the environment.

Action needed to support lions and ecosystem services

If Africa is to support a rapidly expanding human population and a growing economy, countries must invest in ecosystem services as essential life-support mechanisms. A range of actions are needed:

- Measure and communicate the value of ecosystem services (actual and potential) to all sectors of society
- Rebuild ecosystem services to improve food, carbon, water and human security in sub-Saharan Africa
- Use the market for these ecosystem services to support conservation throughout the lion range
- Create business models that support both ecosystem services and lions
- Create conservation models that reflect the needs of human communities
- Encourage policy makers to consider these benefits (and their potential loss)
- Encourage governments and international donors to invest in lion conservation
- Recognise the significance of the continent's unique biodiversity in shaping and sustaining Africa's cultural heritage
- Restore lion populations as an indicator of healthy ecosystem services

Lions are on a knife edge throughout sub-Saharan Africa. Their decline is a tragedy for the whole world. And if Africa loses more lions, many countries will not only lose the direct economic benefits that they bring through tourism and trophy hunting, but likely also a host of other ecosystem services that come from the threatened habitats through which they stalk.

Lionscapes provide a larger than average contribution to Africa's **ecosystem services**; the many benefits humans receive from healthy ecosystems

Senegal

'Lions of Teranga' are the national football team in **Senegal**.

see page 74

<50

One of the flagship projects of Revealing **Benin**, Pendjari National Park is projected to create some 6,000 jobs and over US$25 million in export earnings.

see page 88

100-500

Benin

Chad

Central African Republic

Cameroon

Waza National Park, **Cameroon**, includes important genetic resources such as wild rice (*Oryza barthii*) and Sorghum sp. in the Yaéré floodplains.

see page 63

<50

Trade in devil's claw (*Harpagophytum procumbens*), a tuber used in medicine, is a multi-million dollar business in **Namibia** including in Bwabwata National Park.

see page 66

<50

Seasonal floods ensure the vast grasslands of Zakouma National Park in **Chad**, where lions and pastoralists co-exist.

see page 59

100-500

Angola

Namibia

South Africa

The floodplain of the Kafue Flats in **Zambia** helps to prevent downstream flooding and provides rich fisheries resources.

see page 38

100-500

The Luangwa wetland in **Zambia** provides fisheries valued at over US$5 million a year.

see page 52

500+

Estimated lion numbers in lionscapes which provide major ecosystem services

  <50   **50-100** **100-500** **500+**

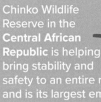
Chinko Wildlife Reserve in the **Central African Republic** is helping bring stability and safety to an entire region; and is its largest employer and taxpayer.[16]

see page 76 **<50**

  $19,000 **100-500**
Each lion in the Queen Elizabeth National Park, **Uganda** has been estimated at a value of nearly US$19,000 per year in tourism revenue.

see page 24

Alatash National Park in **Ethiopia** was established in 2006 primarily to protect against desertification.

see page 58 **<50**

Group ranches in **Kenya** are encouraging co-existence with lions by supporting more effective cattle ranching, reaching markets worth more than US$1 million annually.

see page 55 **100-500**

Ethiopia

Uganda

Kenya

The extensive miombo forests of **Tanzania** are an important national carbon store.

see page 42 **500+**

Tanzania

Zambia

Mozambique

The sustainable management practices of the forestry company LevasFlor in **Mozambique** are helping link lion territories in the Gorongosa National Park and Marromeu Special Reserve.

see page 60 **100-500**

Zimbabwe

The Chyulu Hills, part of Kenya's Amboseli-Tsavo ecosystem, supply water to nearly seven million people including the residents of Mombasa. It has a REDD+ carbon project, tourism conservancies and livestock compensation programme.

see page 51 **500+**

The lion is a totemic animal for the Shona people in **Zimbabwe**.

see page 70 **500+**

Trade in the mopane worm (*Imbrasia belina*) across **South Africa**, is worth US$30-50 million per year, Kruger National Park is exploring mopane worm harvesting in its northern region.

see page 54 **500+**

Lion range based on extant and possibly extinct Species Survival Commission data: https://www.iucnredlist.org/species/15951/115130419#geographic-range[11]

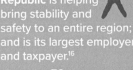

2. Lions and ecosystems

"The water that quenches our thirst, the air that we breathe, the trees that provide shade, and the animals that give us company, all make life real and creation complete."

Maasai Elder[1]

© WCS

Lions in the landscape

After humans, it is thought that lions (*Panthera leo*) once had the widest geographic distribution of all land mammals, extending from South Africa, across Eurasia and to the eastern seaboard of North America.[2] Apart from a small population in India, today's lions are scattered across a few increasingly isolated patches of Africa. Most are found in just a quarter of the great African savannahs, covering some 3.4 million km². And shockingly, within this range, only 10 areas (four in East Africa and six in Southern Africa) have been identified as offering a secure future for lions. Elsewhere populations are under serious threat of local extinction.[3,4,5]

Although lions generally live in fairly small social units, they are truly landscape species. Their territories can spread over hundreds of kilometres; even their roar, the loudest of all the big cats, can be heard up to 8 km away. To thrive, lions need to disperse; this is only possible if suitable habitat and prey is available – in large landscapes or when smaller habitat patches are connected through effective networks of ecological corridors.[6]

The challenge is clear: to find, plan and implement development that protects ecosystem services, delivers a wide range of benefits to local and more distant communities, and conserves Africa's unique biodiversity

Lions share their habitat with a huge diversity of other species, and despite dramatic declines[7] these landscapes remain some of the most diverse on Earth for mammals,[8] birds[9] and other biodiversity.[10] Stable populations of carnivores are useful indicators of healthy and connected landscapes.[11]

It is clear that large, intact, healthy and connected landscapes are vital for lions to survive and thrive. But important questions remain in the minds of many African governments regarding how this land can be managed and financed, and indeed whether it is worth the expense and effort to preserve these areas compared to the other benefits that could come from using them in alternative ways, e.g. for agriculture. This report focuses on the benefits that these lion landscapes or "lionscapes" bring in addition to the long-term security of wild lion populations.

LIONS IN CRISIS

The focus here is on examples of intact, or fairly intact, landscapes that are safeguarding both lions and essential ecosystem services. But such good examples are becoming harder to find – and the positive benefits described in this report should not detract from the ongoing crisis that lions are facing. Lions have disappeared from 92% of their historical range and numbers have declined from perhaps 200,000 a hundred years ago to somewhere between 20,000 and 30,000 today.[12] Climate change is adding to these pressures.[13,14] As lion habitat and numbers collapse, so do the ecosystem services upon which Africa relies. This situation is not helped by the fact that funding of protected areas, where over 50% of the remaining lion range is concentrated, is so low in most African countries that there is a risk they may lose much of their remaining wildlife resources before human communities have the chance to benefit from them in economic terms.[15]

The challenge is clear: to find, plan and implement development that protects ecosystem services, delivers a wide range of benefits to local and more distant communities, and conserves Africa's unique biodiversity. Understanding the interconnectedness of land, the way it is used and the services it provides are essential first steps.

Biodiversity: Driving political momentum for nature conservation

Lions are increasingly the focus of national and international diplomacy.[1] Large carnivores attract significant attention from politicians and have the potential to raise awareness about a wide range of other threatened species. Two conventions, the Convention on International Trade in Endangered Species of Wild Fauna and Flora (CITES) and the Convention on the Conservation of Migratory Species of Wild Animals (CMS), have recently focused attention on the conservation of large carnivores in general, and lions specifically. In 2017, the two conventions established a joint CMS-CITES African Carnivores Initiative to support the implementation of resolutions and decisions on lions, cheetahs, leopards and wild dogs by developing a pan-African strategy for lion conservation[2] and promoting human–carnivore coexistence.

However, despite the number of these global conservation treaties across the lion range, lions have continued to decline.[3] While domestic interest in African conservation is increasing, it all too often gets sidelined in a rush for economic development. **An understanding that natural ecosystems are not just wasted space, but provide services of concrete and irreplaceable value to a modern society, is a critical step in tipping the balance back in favour of lions and other wild species.**

In policy terms, integrating the need to safeguard lion populations into the interests of other conventions like the UN Framework Convention on Climate Change and the UN Convention to Combat Desertification can help to bring the conservation debate to the attention of other important stakeholders. Similarly, lions can be used as a flagship species when reviewing the contribution of healthy intact ecosystems for delivering the Sustainable Development Goals (see map). Finally, but most importantly, there is a need to vastly improve the implementation of treaty commitments at local and national-scale, moving from plans and commitments to actual conservation actions, outputs and outcomes funded by the international community and focused on achieving the conservation successes perceived within the many global conservation orientated treaties.[4]

An understanding that natural ecosystems are not just wasted space, but provide services of concrete and irreplaceable value to a modern society, is a critical step in tipping the balance back in favour of lions and other wild species

The whole lion range contributes to the achievement of the Sustainable Development Goals, with particularly high contributions in East Africa where nature and human populations are in close proximity

The contribution of the lion range to Sustainable Development Goals (SDG)

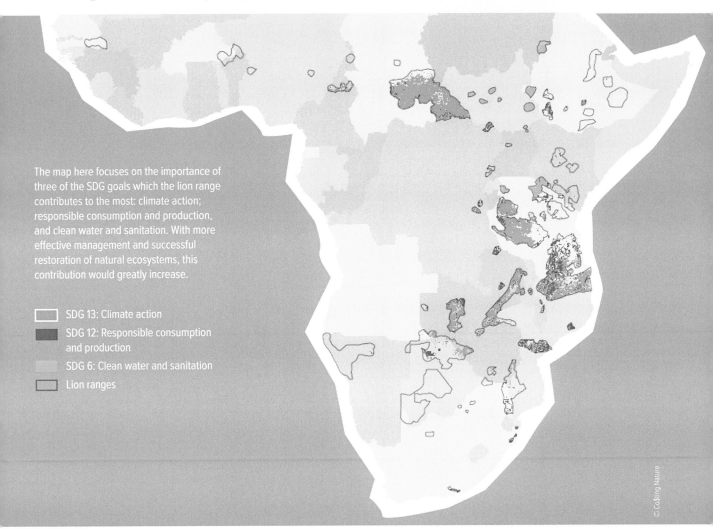

The map here focuses on the importance of three of the SDG goals which the lion range contributes to the most: climate action; responsible consumption and production, and clean water and sanitation. With more effective management and successful restoration of natural ecosystems, this contribution would greatly increase.

- SDG 13: Climate action
- SDG 12: Responsible consumption and production
- SDG 6: Clean water and sanitation
- Lion ranges

© Co$ting Nature

Ecosystem services: An introduction

Ecosystem services include any benefits that humans receive from healthy, properly-functioning ecosystems. These include:[2]

- **Supporting services:** the basic ecological functions that maintain life such as photosynthesis, soil formation and nutrient cycling.
- **Provisioning services:** including contributions to food and water security, and the supply of medicines and other materials.
- **Regulating services:** such as prevention of flooding, landslides and soil erosion and the mitigation of climate change.
- **Cultural services:** covering benefits ranging from recreational, historical and aesthetic values to the importance of iconic species to people around the world and of particular natural sites for various faiths and belief systems.

There is good evidence that biodiversity plays a key role in ecosystem services[3] and that the more species of wild plants and animals present, the more resilient the ecosystem will be to climate change[4] and other environmental disruption.[5] Research in southern Africa showed considerable overlap between biodiversity and a range of ecosystem services (surface water supply, water flow regulation, carbon storage, soil accumulation and soil retention).[6] Conserving critical sites for biodiversity therefore often provides disproportionate benefits to people.[7] Many but by no means all ecosystem services can be measured easily in economic terms.[8] As an example of less easily quantifiable benefits, the concept of ecosystem services includes a wide range of cultural, emotional and aesthetic values which are important for many more reasons than economics.

Africa's ecosystems generate flows of goods and services that help secure the livelihood of more than 62% of the continent's rural population, over 300 million people in sub-Saharan Africa,[9] and Africa is the last place on Earth with a significant assemblage of large mammals.[10] Bearing these two facts in mind, the focus of this report is on ecosystem benefits emerging from lionscapes throughout Africa. Our research confirms that such ecosystems do not just support iconic species such as the lion, but in doing so also and fortuitously supply a wide range of other benefits.

> Our research confirms that ecosystems do not just support iconic species such as the lion, but in doing so also and fortuitously supply a wide range of other benefits

Provisioning

Regulating

Cultural

Supporting

Summary of ecosystem services

"Without biodiversity and its provisions and services there would be no development."

Cristiana Pasca Palmer, UN Assistant Secretary General
and Executive Secretary of the Convention on Biological Diversity[1]

3. Lions directly support ecosystem services

"[Lions] ... are now a top foreign exchange earner to the country contributing 10% of GDP and 23% of the total foreign exports."

Hon. Prof. Ephraim Kamuntu, Minister of Tourism, Wildlife and Antiquities, Uganda[11]

Lion tourism:
A key element

The draw of the big five mammals (lion, black rhino *Diceros bicornis*, buffalo *Syncerus caffer,* leopard *Panthera pardus* and savannah elephant *Loxodonta africana*) is undoubtedly of unique value to tourism in sub-Saharan Africa. Tourism can be characterised by two very different approaches: wildlife watching (e.g. photographic tourism) and trophy hunting (see page 30). Both approaches are common throughout the lion range.

Wildlife watching is a very important segment of tourism for most African countries, representing 80% of the total annual sales of trips to Africa, with the 'safari' as the most popular product.[1] Foreign tourists contributed over US$30 billion to the countries of sub-Saharan Africa in 2017.[2] And lions are a favourite with visitors to protected areas.[3] For private landowners, for example, lions are amongst the most sought after animals for photographic safaris and trophy hunting.[4] In particular, these and other charismatic mega-fauna have a vital flagship role by attracting most overseas and first-time visitors to protected areas.[5] Visitor interviews in Kruger National Park in South Africa identify large predators as the most attractive incentive for visitors and most important for influencing visitors' behaviour.[6] An assessment of photos of African species loaded on Flickr found lions' pictures were uploaded well over two times more than any other species.[7]

Richness of large wildlife species is positively related to income derived from ecotourism.[8] If charismatic species disappear, the economic losses can be great. Visitor surveys in Uganda found nearly 40% would want to see the park entry fees reduced if large cats were not to be seen.[9] Each lion in the Queen Elizabeth National Park has been estimated at a value of nearly US$19,000 per year (updated to 2019 prices[10]) in tourism revenue.[11] However, these figures need to be treated with caution; the tourist draw is more to do with the presence or absence of lions rather than the exact number of lions in the landscape and there will be a law of diminishing returns (a park with 200 lions would not get twice the visitors of a park with a hundred lions). In response to the recent increase in elephant poaching in Africa, researchers have assessed that the associated lost economic benefits via tourism could reach US$25 million annually.[12] Rwanda lost its lions, but their reintroduction to Akagera National Park has been linked to rising tourists.[13]

Tourism revenue can also play a critical role in livelihoods and community development; although the extent to which economic benefits reach local people varies as does opportunities for local communities to participate

Tourism potential

Tourism is concentrated in only a few countries in sub-Saharan Africa – and within those countries it is restricted to a handful of sites. Expanding tourism will depend on:

• Protecting the wildlife resource more effectively
• Investing in infrastructure
• Improving political stability
• Marketing
• Ease of access

Lions are amongst the most sought after animals for photographic safaris

© Sebastian Kennerknecht, Panthera, APU

directly in tourism provision. Each staff member in the tourism industry supports four to seven dependents in rural areas with low employment opportunities, and rural populations tend to spend wages within the community, furthering the multiplier effect.[14] Benefits arise from direct income support, employment by the protected area or through associated economic options (work in hotels, homestays, craft sales, etc.). In Uganda, the Uganda Wildlife Authority shares revenue with local communities.[15] In Tanzania, Serengeti National Park generates jobs,[16] and contributes significant amounts of money to local development projects.[17] In Murchison Falls, Uganda, the incomes from sale of local products and services reached nearly US$200,000, one indication of the associated benefits of tourism.[18] Community organisations

Protected areas where photographic tourism is the primary land use tended to be more effective for conserving lions and prey and have higher management budgets

© Sue Stolton

in the Okavango Delta, Botswana, benefit from contracts and joint venture partnerships with safari operators, plus sale of hunting quotas, crafts and small-scale tourism ventures.[19] A study of Kruger National Park in South Africa suggests that **wildlife conservation linked to ecotourism is 18 times more profitable than using land for livestock and crops.**[20]

Protected areas where photographic tourism is the primary land use tended to be more effective for conserving lions and/or their prey and have higher management budgets.[21] Promoting appropriate tourism in protected areas is likely to yield long-term benefits such as reducing threats to wildlife.[22] As wildlife-based tourism is likely to continue to grow in Africa,[23] over-visitation in some of the most popular protected areas is clearly a risk.[24] This creates growth opportunities, both for smaller protected areas in countries that already have a large tourist footprint, such as Botswana, Kenya, Namibia, South Africa, Tanzania and Zimbabwe, and for a large-scale increase in visitors to protected areas in countries that are currently missing from many travel itineraries. Mozambique and Zambia are two countries with large protected area networks and largely stable politics that are in an excellent position to expand ecotourism. However, both would need to invest substantially in infrastructure and increase management effectiveness [25,26,27] and in applying existing laws regarding poaching, and in the case of Mozambique, reducing habitat loss in protected areas associated with unrestricted human settlement, illegal mining and illegal logging.

Tourism's contribution to the economy of selected lion range countries[28]

GDP (direct contribution):	Direct employment:
Tanzania = 9.4%	Tanzania = 7.1%
Kenya = 5.2%	Kenya = 2.8%
Namibia = 8%	Namibia = 6.5%
Zambia = 6.5%	Zambia = 5%
Zimbabwe = 3.5%	Zimbabwe = 3.4%
South Africa = 2.4%	South Africa = 1%
Malawi = 2.8%	Malawi = 1.5%[29]

Conservancies: recognising the role of ecosystem services

Legislation in several African countries supports the development of conservancies by local communities on their own communal land. These are managed primarily for wildlife, while at the same time encouraging the community to work with private companies to create and manage ecotourism ventures, trophy hunting and associated trades such as crafts and community forest management.[1] This devolution of user-rights over wildlife to landholders led to the development of conservancies over vast areas in Kenya (11% of country[2,3]), South Africa (2.5%[4]), Namibia (19.6%[5]) and Zimbabwe. Characteristics of conservancies often include increased tolerance to carnivores, possibly because of better livestock husbandry, reduced prevalence of game fencing and increased importance of wildlife-based income.[6]

The development and expansion of community conservancies in Kenya have been identified by the government as an *"important and exciting innovative conservation solution"*[7]. Over 160 conservancies, which currently cover 6.46 million hectares,[8] have succeeded in providing multiple benefits to local people such as employment, healthcare, education, security, better management of livestock, etc. But such schemes are only likely to be successful if they have sustainable sources of funding,[9,10] such as associated tourism ventures or carbon financing.[11] Conservancies directly impact the lives of more than 700,000 people in Kenya and secure 65% of the country's wildlife outside national parks and reserves. Lions have benefitted from the creation of community conservancies[12] and help provide a tourist attraction. Across Kenya conservancies manage 142 tourist facilities, earning some US$3 million a year.[13]

The Maasai Wilderness Conservation Trust (MWCT) is an NGO that has collaborated with local Maasai leaders and communities in the Tsavo/ Amboseli ecosystem, creating a partnership which is protecting the natural resources of the area and securing a critical wildlife corridor between Tsavo and Amboseli National Parks. Community-based programmes in conservation, health and education have been set up by MWCT, resulting in the employment of over 300 local people as Community Rangers and

Conservancies directly impact the lives of more than 700,000 people in Kenya and secure 65% of the country's wildlife outside national parks and reserves

Lion (Simba[14]) Scouts (researching and protecting lions and other wildlife), teachers, nurses, etc. Three areas within the community Group Ranch have been secured as conservancies purely for the use of wildlife. MWCT and its tourism partner, Campi ya Kanzi, contribute jointly US$2,500,000 into the community, per year. A Payment for Ecosystem Services (PES) tourism surcharge funds a Wildlife Pays programme that compensates livestock herders for losses to wildlife predation through a rigorous multi-layered verification system and monitoring of best husbandry practices.[15] This model of livestock compensation, and other community conservation programmes, draws on similar initiatives such as those developed by Big Life Foundation[16]; together these two entities implement conservation interventions over the majority of the Amboseli ecosystem.

Trophy hunting of lions

One of the most direct ways to value lions is through their attraction to trophy hunters, a niche but high revenue tourism approach. Ten years ago, it was estimated that across the 11 main big game hunting countries (South Africa, Namibia, Tanzania, Botswana, Zimbabwe, Zambia, Cameroon, Central African Republic, Ethiopia, Burkina Faso, Benin), the surface area occupied by hunting concessions was 110 million hectares, almost 15% of the total land area of these countries,[1] and in several cases greater than the area of protected areas. This total has decreased since then, but the area is still considerable and can help protect habitats from other land uses, such as conversion to agriculture,[2] and provide alternative and complementary income sources from wildlife.[3] Hunting thus creates incentives for the retention of large blocks of state, community and private land for wildlife while also protecting wider ecosystem services.

Factors which tend to promote trophy hunting over other wildlife tourism include lack of tourist infrastructure, inaccessibility, political instability, limited scenic qualities, and the dominance of a few well-known areas such as Serengeti for photographic tourism making diversification challenging. In some countries, e.g. Zimbabwe, catering to a small number of high-paying foreign tourists was seen as a necessity when political instability reduced the number of photo-tourists.[4,5] Lions are often hunted in areas adjacent to a fully protected source population[6] and considerable attention is given to management issues and optimal densities of lions to ensure sustainability of the hunting concessions.[7,8,9]

Hunting fees and revenues are substantial for those directly involved; with lion hunts attracting the highest mean prices (between US$24,000–US$71,000) of all trophy species; and thus generating significant revenue for wildlife authorities.[10] However, overall hunting contributions to GDP are probably less important than other forms of tourism, with figures in dispute. Pro-hunting organisations suggest that eight countries (South Africa, Namibia, Zimbabwe, Botswana, Ethiopia, Mozambique, Tanzania and Zambia) received revenues from hunters of US$326 million a year and supported over 50,000 jobs,[11] whilst anti-hunting organisations estimate a contribution of less than US$132 million per year.[12]

There is a vigorous debate around the status of trophy hunting within lion conservation, and whether it should be considered as a threat to wild populations or as a sustainable form of management and source of conservation finance

Hunting proponents

point out that hunting fees and revenues are substantial, generating significant revenue for wildlife authorities and that critics have failed to come up with alternative revenue generating options for hunting blocks.

Opponents of hunting

stress that revenues from hunting are inadequate to yield high quality wildlife management, that off-takes have negative impacts on populations and that hunting for trophies is inherently unethical.

© Peter Lindsey

Sport hunting in Niassa in northern
Mozambique helps operational costs
including anti-poaching activities.

© Niassa Lion Project

Niassa is a vast protected area of 42,200 km² in northern Mozambique with a healthy population of lions.[13] The protected area is divided into 17 management units allocated for ecotourism and sport hunting. Hunting fees fund 30% of the annual operational costs of the reserve as well as anti-poaching and management activities,[14] although hunting revenues do not necessarily compensate for financial losses of livestock at the household level.[15] Tanzania contains up to half of the global population of free-ranging lions and is also the main location for lion trophy hunting in Africa. Hunting occurs on some 86% of protected land[16]; however, a growing proportion of hunting blocks are falling vacant – due an apparent contraction of the industry. Similarly in West Africa, just over 40% of the vast W-Arly Pendjari ecosystem of Benin, Burkina Faso and Niger is leased as hunting areas to private operators who take over management responsibilities for the areas. 75% of the meat harvested from these hunts is provided to neighbouring communities, between 30-50% of revenue is fed back to local associations and the concessions are major employers.[17]

There is a vigorous debate around the status of trophy hunting within lion conservation, and whether it should be considered as a threat to wild populations or as a sustainable form of management and source of conservation finance.[18,19,20] Furthermore, there are concerns that current hunting levels are unsustainable. Hunting is usually focused on older males.[21] This has wider impacts because the males that replace these older lions in the pride kill cubs they have not fathered.[22] In Tanzania, higher profits are also being linked to less sustainable, short-term operations.[23] Concerns over sustainability, and the ethics of hunting, have led to increased scrutiny of issues[24] related to hunting and some[25] site moratoriums on hunting.[26] Several countries ban lion trophy imports and some airlines will not transport trophies.[27] Revenues from hunting may decline as pressures against hunting grow, leaving a major gap in funding.[28] This could have negative consequences for lions, by undermining the competitiveness of wildlife-based land uses and by undermining tolerance for co-existence,[29] and the ecosystem services these lionscapes protect. This threat is particularly acute in cases where hunting blocks fall vacant. Such areas then become highly vulnerable to human pressures and to political pressure for reallocation to alternative land uses.

There is an urgent need to develop alternatives to trophy hunting which ensure that areas currently or formerly used for hunting are retained within the wildlife estate, that generate significant revenues from and for wildlife management, and which effectively protect lions and their habitats. One potential example is the establishment of frameworks to allow philanthropic conservation investors to obtain leases for hunting concessions for non-hunting purposes, and/or to utilise carbon credit or development off-set schemes to pay for the protection of former hunting blocks.

4. Lion conservation also supports other ecosystem services

"If you want to continue getting water for agriculture, you need to maintain a landscape that produces rain."

Kaddu Sebunya, head of the African Wildlife Foundation[1]

Ecosystem services from lionscapes

The economic benefits of both wildlife tourism and trophy hunting are important sources of revenue at local and national level, but are actually a small part of the total ecosystem services available from lionscapes. Far more significant than values directly related to lions are the values from natural ecosystems containing lions. Research carried out for this report found that **lionscapes provide more ecosystem services than the average across Africa.**[2]

The message is clear, money invested in lion and other forms of conservation also produces benefits in terms of multiple supporting, provisioning and regulating services. We provide a brief overview of some of the most important on the following pages.

Provisioning

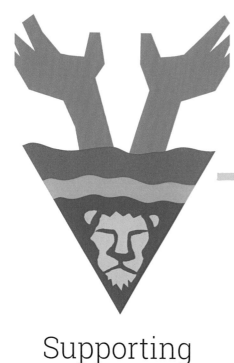

Supporting

Regulating

Cultural

Lionscapes provide more ecosystem services than the average across Africa

medicine

water

genetic resources

materials (wood etc)

food

climate

soil fertility

hazard regulation

pollination

carbon capture

water flow/purification

tourism

peace & stability

cultural identity

Saving the land: Disaster risk reduction

Degradation of natural ecosystems increases the risks of weather-related disaster.[4] In the context of lionscapes, critical issues relate to the twin extremes of drought and flood, and more pervasive threats from soil erosion and desertification. Drought can increase independent of rainfall, due to the reduced capacity of land to capture and hold water. It has been estimated that on severely degraded land as little as 5% of total rainfall is used productively.[5]

Increased run-off on degraded land leaves areas more prone to flooding, further increasing the loss of top soil and biodiversity.[6] Natural landscapes provide opportunities for flood dispersal. Kafue Flats is a floodplain covering 6,500 km^2 in Zambia. The area includes several protected areas including Kafue National Park, one of the largest in Africa and seen as vital for the future viability of lions. The floodplain helps to prevent downstream flooding and also provides rich fisheries resources, although hydrology has already been altered by hydroelectric development and land conversion,[7]

Disaster relief

One of the often overlooked benefits of protected areas is that they have the infrastructure and capacity to help victims of disasters. Cyclone Idai in March 2019 was one of most disastrous tropical cyclones recorded in the South-West Indian Ocean basin. Impacts where felt across Mozambique, Zimbabwe and Malawi, including in the buffer zone of Gorongosa National Park in central Mozambique home to some 150 lions. Staff from the park helped deliver food by helicopter and distribute it among local people.

and further dam construction threatens these ecosystem services. Disasters like the 2000 flood in Mozambique, which killed 800 people and caused US$450 million of damage,[8] are made worse by overgrazing and land degradation,[9] poorly managed forests[10] and vegetation clearance[11] including deforestation.[12] In 2019, further devastating floods have hit Mozambique with protected areas immediately playing a vital role in mitigation and providing disaster relief.[13]

Desertification affects 45% of Africa's land area with 55% of this area at high or very high risk of further degradation.[14] Sand and dust storms have increased 25-50% over the last century due to a combination of land degradation and climate change.[15] Soil erosion also has major impacts on hydropower, impacts which are estimated at US$12 million (converted to 2019 values[16]) in Malawi.[17] Natural ecosystems play a critical role in preventing extreme weather events and earth movements from developing into human disasters caused by flooding, landslides, dust storms and desertification.[18] Natural vegetation is a major and cost effective stabilising factor to control erosion, dust storms,[19] dune formation

Disaster risk reduction strategies are increasingly looking to management of natural resources alongside or instead of traditional engineering approaches

and desertification. Disaster risk reduction strategies are increasingly looking to management of natural resources alongside or instead of traditional engineering approaches,[20] with protected areas and other forms of area-based conservation recognised as an important tool.[21] Impacts of drought are also affected by land use patterns; the Shompole-Olkiramatian ecosystem in Kenya, for example, where traditional Maasai pastoralism is maintained within a lionscape, showed considerable resilience during drought in 2009 compared to neighbouring areas.[22]

Desertification across southern Africa is likely to be exacerbated by climate change.[23] The Fish River Nature Reserve, Baviaanskloof Nature Reserve and Addo Elephant National Park are protected areas in the Albany Thicket Biome of South Africa, an area of high conservation value which also provides water for surrounding urban areas. Lions have been reintroduced into Addo Elephant National Park.[24] From 2007-2013, a major restoration project aimed to reduce threats of desertification in the area. Restoring degraded lands increases vegetation cover, improves the potential for water infiltration, reduces soil erosion, increases carbon sequestration and provides alternative land use options. Use of spekboom (*Portulacaria afra*), a native species, helps to ensure success, because it has a high rate of primary production and provides conditions for additional species to establish, preventing a monoculture from developing. Spekboom also significantly increases soil moisture.[25]

All told, analysis suggests that **the lion range provides 11% of Africa's potential disaster risk reduction services, including erosion control, coastal protection, flood mitigation and flow regulation, on 6.7% of the continent's area. Importantly some 73% of these hazard mitigation services are within protected areas**.[26] But not all these protected areas are currently being managed effectively, and the status of the 'unprotected' areas remains uncertain.

Protected areas provide vital hazard mitigation services across Africa

© Sgt. Cary Humphries

Flooded Central Mozambique on March 20, 2000, Tech. Sgt. Cary Humphries, U.S. Air (https://en.wikipedia.org/wiki/2000_Mozambique_flood#/media/File:An_MH-53M_Pave_Low_IV_helicopter_approaches_the_refueling_basket_of_an_MC-130P_Combat_Shadow.jpg)

"...strengthen the sustainable use and management of ecosystems and implement integrated environmental and natural resource management approaches that incorporate disaster risk reduction."

Sendai Framework for Disaster Risk Reduction 2015-2030[3]

Hazard mitigation benefits across the lion range

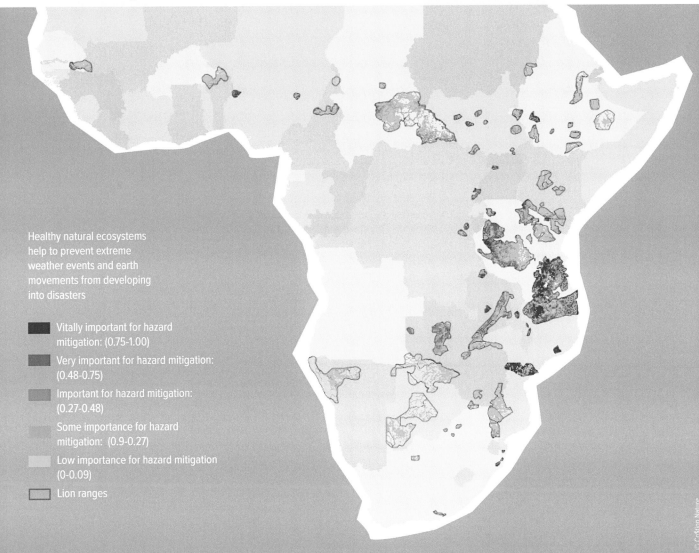

Healthy natural ecosystems help to prevent extreme weather events and earth movements from developing into disasters

- Vitally important for hazard mitigation: (0.75-1.00)
- Very important for hazard mitigation: (0.48-0.75)
- Important for hazard mitigation: (0.27-0.48)
- Some importance for hazard mitigation: (0.9-0.27)
- Low importance for hazard mitigation (0-0.09)
- Lion ranges

© Co$ing Nature

Storing carbon, mitigating climate change in lionscapes

Over the past decade, there has been increasing recognition of the importance of natural resource management as a means of storing and sequestering carbon to mitigate climate change. A range of incentive schemes have emerged, most notably Reducing Emissions from Deforestation and Degradation (REDD+). Protected areas are seen as having a key role in securing REDD objectives,[2] although working out the logistics and politics of this has taken some time.

Closed-canopy forests and peat soils are the largest terrestrial carbon stores,[3] neither of which are likely lion habitat, but the role of miombo woodland, grassland and savannah remains significant. Despite arid areas having low plant biomass, and hence relatively low organic carbon in vegetation and soil, inorganic soil carbon increases as aridity increases. Research suggests that tropical dry forests remain overall carbon sinks, for example in Zambia.[4] Dryland soil organic reserves represent 27% of the global total.[5] Some calculations suggest that the proportionately faster rate of loss of grasslands, coupled with degradation due to soil erosion and overgrazing, means that total carbon loss from grasslands and savannahs could be equivalent to that from deforestation.[6] Southern Africa's miombo dry land forests cover 2.4 million km² (twice the area of the Congo Basin rainforests).[7] Although miombo forests only store 10-20% of the carbon as closed-canopy forest in Tanzania, the far larger area of miombo means that it is a more important national carbon store overall[8] and there is a large potential for carbon storage if management could be made more sustainable.[9] Yet miombo woodland is everywhere under threat, with above-ground biomass declining.[10] Woodlands can permanently lose species when they are cleared. Even if trees are then allowed to regenerate, the woodland structure may have changed and the lost species may not return.[11]

Much depends on where the carbon is stored and how it recovers from disturbance. Research in Mozambique found that miombo woodland carbon stocks were 110 tC/ha, with 76 tC/ha in the soil carbon pool and the rest in tree stems, roots and saplings.[12] Slash and burn agriculture depleted soil carbon in miombo woodland. Although abandonment of land results in recovery of above-ground biomass and thus carbon within a few decades, soil carbon stocks take much longer to recover.[13] Measurements in Malawi found agricultural soils contained on average 40% less carbon than natural woodland.[14] In Zambia, forest structure and above-ground carbon storage recovered 20 years after abandonment and agricultural fallows are seen to have major potential for carbon-based ecosystem storage schemes.[15]

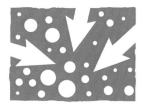

The voluntary carbon market could provide the incentive necessary to drive more sustainable management and provide suitable habitat for lions and associated species

The lion range covers just 6.7% of Africa's land, but already contributes 11% of Africa's carbon storage and sequestration

So loss of carbon through forest clearance produces long-term carbon losses that cannot be quickly or easily reversed, strengthening arguments for retention of natural ecosystems in an intact state.

The lion range covers just 6.7% of Africa's land, but already contributes 11% of Africa's carbon storage and sequestration (see map).[16] The voluntary carbon market could provide the incentive necessary to drive more sustainable management,[17] and thus also provide suitable habitat for lions and associated species. In Tanzania, for example, over US$750[18] million per year could potentially be earned from REDD+ if woodland management strategies to reduce deforestation and degradation were fully[19] developed and implemented.

REDD+ and lions

Malawi: The Kulera Landscape REDD+ programme targets over 65,000 households (350,000 people) living in rural communities in the border zone of three protected areas co-managed by local communities and the government. Malawi is one of the poorest countries in the world and a landscape-based REDD+ approach that works directly through a community association is the most dependable path for conservation-based sustainable development. The project partners are the Department of National Parks and Wildlife (DNPW), the Nyika-Vwaza Association (NVA), the Nkhotakota Wildlife Reserve Association (NAWIRA), and Terra Global.[20] The overall goals of the programme are to reduce deforestation and protect wildlife through livelihood improvements and managing natural resources as an asset base to capture long-term economic benefits.[21]

Kenya: A long-term project on the land between Tsavo East and Tsavo West National Parks has restored overgrazed and poached out land into 200,000 ha of dryland Acacia-Commiphora forest, which is home to 15-30 lions, offsets 1 million tons of CO_2 emissions a year and supports an impressive range of community initiatives including a carbon neutral, fair trade clothing factory.[22] Nearby, the 410,000 ha Chyulu Hills REDD+ project supports a wildlife corridor linking Amboseli, Chyulu Hills and Tsavo National Park. The project was launched in 2017 and is expected to avoid nearly 30m tons of CO_2 emissions over its 30-year lifetime. The project achieved Gold Level validation and verification under the Verified Carbon Standard and the Climate, Community and Biodiversity Standards, and secured over two million carbon credits for sale from its first monitoring period (2013-2016).[23]

Tanzania: Carbon Tanzania is a social enterprise working with communities to realise the economic value of standing forests, mainly through the sale of carbon offsets. In Makame Wildlife Management Area, close to Tarangire National Park, 104,000 ha is being protected through collaboration with five Maasai villages consisting of around 15,000 people. Traditional grazing patterns are being maintained and illegal settlement, responsible for loss of forest in the region, is being prevented.[24]

Total carbon loss from grasslands and savannahs could be equivalent to that from deforestation

Relative potential and realised carbon services
from the lion range[1]

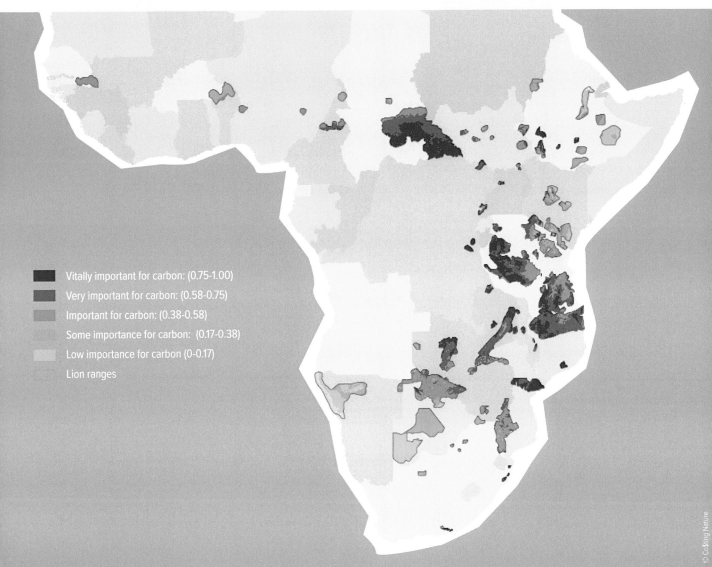

Vitally important for carbon: (0.75-1.00)

Very important for carbon: (0.58-0.75)

Important for carbon: (0.38-0.58)

Some importance for carbon: (0.17-0.38)

Low importance for carbon (0-0.17)

Lion ranges

© Co$ting Nature

Lion Carbon: financing conservation in Zambia

The search for long-term finance that can simultaneously support the conservation of wildlife and the livelihoods of local communities is far from simple. Payments for Ecosystem Services (PES) have been heralded as a major opportunity.[1] PES schemes reward the generation of clearly-defined ecosystem services. They are often developed for services which have no established market, making it necessary to introduce new reward and compensation systems.[2]

Carbon schemes are the most common PES in Africa, due to the possibly exaggerated[3] international demand for this service by voluntary carbon markets.[4] Since greenhouse gases mix in the atmosphere, donors have tended to locate emission reductions where investment costs are relatively low and deforestation rates are high.[5] Donors have pledged over US$5 billion[6] to the Green Climate Fund (GCF), which aims to disburse around US$2.5 billion a year toward climate mitigation and adaptation projects in developing countries, including payments for REDD+ and sustainable forest management, conservation of forests and enhancement of carbon sink projects.[7] Carbon accounting methodologies, such as the Gold Standard and Verified Carbon Standard, have made it possible to assess the real and additional emission reductions required and have boosted forest-based schemes.[8] REDD+ strategies also have the advantage of including strong community participation and equitable benefit sharing.[9] Carbon pricing is also widely variable with prices varying from less than US$1/gigaton of carbon dioxide equivalent ($GtCO_2e$) to a maximum of US$139/$tCO_2e$.[10]

Deforestation is a major issue in Zambia.[11] A multi-partnered project has been working on implementing the voluntary carbon market in the country for the last few years to incentivise sustainable forestry. In 2018, for example, the luxury goods company Richemont committed to a seven year programme to reduce their emissions primarily through carbon offset purchases supporting forest conservation and social impact projects in Zambia.[12]

The Lion Carbon project aims to apply a REDD+ scheme over 8,050 km² linking four national parks in Zambia, in a collaborative effort between a social enterprise (Biocarbon Partners) and an Oxford University-based

> Over ten years the project aims to protect ten million hectares of forest, securing one of the last six lions strongholds in Southern Africa, and help the livelihoods of a million people

conservation organisation (Lion Landscapes). The scheme represents a 20-fold increase from a tested pilot project, combining extra anti-poaching patrols with reduced habitat loss and equitable benefits-sharing with local communities. Approximately 67% of the Lower Zambezi/Luangwa ecosystem consists of General Management Areas (GMAs) managed by legally mandated Community Resource Boards (CRBs). Income and benefits from wildlife activities are limited. By selling carbon credits to companies looking to make voluntary purchases of carbon credits to offset their emissions, the Lion Carbon project is securing one of the last six lion strongholds in Southern Africa. Over ten years the project aims to protect ten million hectares of forest and help the livelihoods of a million people. A pilot of the project in Rufunsa Conservancy, started in 2012, has seen prey species increase in numbers and lions return to the area. An additional benefit of the carbon schemes being set up in Zambia is that protected areas are becoming carbon neutral, with all emissions related to tourism being offset, including all international tourist airline travel and conservation management within the park.[13]

The Lion Carbon model

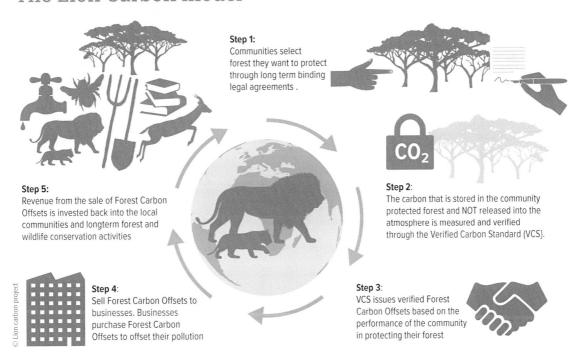

Step 1:
Communities select forest they want to protect through long term binding legal agreements .

Step 2:
The carbon that is stored in the community protected forest and NOT released into the atmosphere is measured and verified through the Verified Carbon Standard (VCS).

Step 3:
VCS issues verified Forest Carbon Offsets based on the performance of the community in protecting their forest

Step 4:
Sell Forest Carbon Offsets to businesses. Businesses purchase Forest Carbon Offsets to offset their pollution

Step 5:
Revenue from the sale of Forest Carbon Offsets is invested back into the local communities and longterm forest and wildlife conservation activities

© Lion carbon project

Resilience to climate change in lionscapes

The lion range in Africa includes some of the most vulnerable and at the same time least prepared countries in the world in terms of coping with climate change. The Intergovernmental Panel on Climate Change (IPCC) has categorised the Zambezi as the river basin exhibiting the 'worst' potential effects of climate change among 11 major African basins, due to the resonating effect of increase in temperature and decrease in rainfall.[2] Climate impacts can affect the very basics of life such as food,[3] water,[4] health,[5] ecosystem services, human habitat and infrastructure.

The ND-GAIN assessment has assessed countries worldwide for their vulnerability to climate change, including: the degree to which a country is exposed to significant climate change from a biophysical perspective; the extent to which a country is dependent upon a sector negatively affected by climate hazard, or the proportion of the population particularly susceptible to a climate change hazard, and the availability of social resources for developing sustainable adaptation solutions. The assessment combines vulnerability with a country's readiness to cope with climate impacts through its ability to leverage investments and convert them into adaptation actions by considering three components: economic readiness, governance readiness and social readiness. **A country's ND-GAIN Score is composed of a vulnerability score and a readiness score.**[6] **18 of the 24 lion range countries fall within the bottom quarter of the index**, and apart from South Africa, all lion range countries fall in the bottom half.[7]

Resilience in this context is the ability of an ecosystem to maintain its functions (biological, chemical and physical) in the face of disturbance. A resilient ecosystem will among other things retain its ecosystem services in the face of climate change. Yet there is a general decline in the resilience of ecosystem functions.[8] Ecosystem-based adaptation will require measures to maintain the resilience of ecosystems under new climatic conditions, so that they can continue to supply essential services. There is a growing consensus amongst conservation biologists that greater biodiversity also confers greater resilience within ecosystems.[9] For instance, ecosystems with high carbon frequently also have high biodiversity,[10] although the mechanisms involved are still subject to debate, and river basins which are managed to retain their flow can help protect, maintain or restore to a certain degree related environmental services.[11] Those responsible for management of natural areas are therefore increasingly looking at options to increase resilience against climate change and other forms of stress.[12, 13] Maintaining the overall resilience of ecosystems in the face of climate change is therefore an overarching aim of virtually all the ecosystem services described here.

A key element regarding resilience to climate change is tourism, which, unlike livestock production or rain-fed agriculture, does not have such a linear relationship with rainfall — and revenues are thus less likely to be affected by increasingly variable rainfall. This, however, does not mean that climate change has no impact on tourism (for example, flooding has impacted tourists accessing areas like the Okavango Delta, whilst drying of the Delta could also reduce visitation if boat access becomes less viable). Nor does it imply that building resilience to climate change impacts is not an important strategy in areas with high tourism values.[14]

"People think the rains come from God and don't look into the future."

Secretary of the Nyangores Water Resource User Associations, Kenya[1]

© Tyrel Bernardini/Ewaso Lions

Saving water

Africa has abundant water resources: with great rivers such as the Congo, Nile, Zambezi and Niger; the second-largest lake in the world, Lake Victoria; significant groundwater supplies and about 10% of the freshwater resources available globally. However, this water is unevenly distributed and Africa is assessed as the second-driest continent on the Earth.[1] 300 million people in sub-Saharan Africa live in water-scarce environments;[2] exacerbated by poor infrastructure.[3,4] Protecting the sources of Africa's water is a vital aspect of water security, along with effective and sustainable planning around both 'blue water' (the surface and groundwater found in lakes, rivers and aquifers) and far more effective use of 'green water' (precipitation on land that is stored in the soil or vegetation and evaporates or transpires through plants).[5] Wetlands also provide many other livelihood benefits; studies in South Africa found a 1 km^2 wetland on average provides natural resources worth US$211 per household per year, over six times the average cash income in the area.[6]

The lion range includes many areas which are important for effective water supply management in sub-Saharan Africa, including areas which have significant inputs into the basins of the great rivers. The range includes areas upstream of major cities particularly in Ethiopia, South Sudan, Uganda and Tanzania (see map).[7] As precipitation has a major impact on the density and range of lions and their prey,[8] the presence and number of lions are indicators of rainfall patterns across many parts of the range.[9]

Malawi: Nyika National Park is the oldest and largest national park in Malawi. Lying about 2000 metres above sea level, the park protects the whole of the 3,200 km^2 Nyika Plateau. 'Nyika' means 'where the water comes from' and the plateau is an important water catchment area in Malawi,[10] feeding into Lake Malawi. The mean annual rainfall in Malawi ranges between 500 mm in low-lying areas to well over 3,000 mm on the high altitude plateaus, such as Nyika.[11] Fifty years ago, Nyika had a healthy population of lions,[12] although populations declined[13] there is hope that Nyika's populations will be restored.[14]

Cameroon: The Waza Logone floodplain in northern Cameroon covers an area of some 8,000 km^2, equalling about 10% of riverine wetlands in the West African Sahel. The area includes Waza National Park, which is home to a small number of lions, one of the few surviving populations in Central Africa.[15] Some 220,000 people are estimated to live in the Waza Logone region, approximately 60% of whom (or 85% of the rural population) rely on floodplain and wetland resources for their basic income and subsistence.[16] The productivity and carrying capacity of the Waza Logone floodplain is highly correlated with the extent of the flooding. In the 1970s, the floodplain was dammed and embankments constructed along the Logone River to

The lion range provides around 7% of Africa's water ecosystem services, with significant inputs in key basins such as the Nile and the Zambezi. The areas upstream of major cities are of high conservation value, particularly in Ethiopia, South Sudan, Uganda and Tanzania.

stimulate irrigated rice cultivation. The impacts, exacerbated by low rainfall, were less productive annual grass-dominated stands, which reduced food sources for wildlife and cattle. In the 1990s the IUCN Waza-Logone project aimed to improve the water availability conditions, specifically in the National Park and adjoining areas, and began a major rehabilitation of the degraded floodplain which led to a recovery of natural resources.[17]

Kenya: The mountains and hills of Kenya are critical for water provision; estimates suggest they contribute to over 3.6% of Kenya's national GDP. Although interest in Kenya's water towers tends to focus on the large mountains (e.g. Mt. Kenya, Mt. Elgon, etc.), the smaller water towers, especially those in the drylands, sustain almost 30% of the country's population and much of its wildlife.[18] The Chyulu Hills-Tsavo West form a volcanic chain in South Eastern Kenya. The area is part of the Amboseli-Tsavo Ecosystem, one of Kenya's lion strongholds.[19] The Chyulu Hills water catchment supplies water to an estimated seven million people downstream, including the residents of Mombasa.[20] Degradation is a problem,[21] but several REDD+ projects (see page 44) are helping secure the area for local people, environmental protection and species conservation.

Relative realised water provisioning services from the lion range

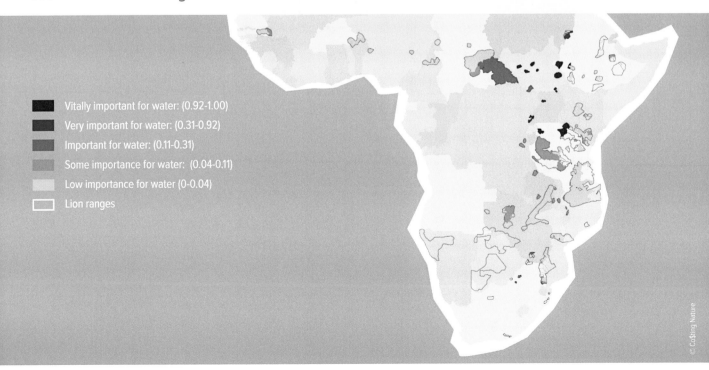

Vitally important for water: (0.92-1.00)
Very important for water: (0.31-0.92)
Important for water: (0.11-0.31)
Some importance for water: (0.04-0.11)
Low importance for water (0-0.04)
Lion ranges

© Co$ing Nature

Luangwa River, Zambia

The Kafue River and the Luangwa River are two of the major tributaries of the Zambezi. The Luangwa is one of the longest remaining free-flowing rivers in Southern Africa.[3] The river's valley includes the South Luangwa National Park and the adjacent Lupande and Lumimba game management areas – an area which holds the largest lion population in Zambia.[4] While the Kafue River is the largest tributary to the Zambezi River, contributing 9% of its water and covers approximately 20% of Zambia's total land area, the Luangwa catchment generates 40% more mean annual runoff than the similarly sized Kafue catchment due to the lack of infrastructure and extraction for irrigation along its course.[5]

The wider economic values of this water provisioning are vast. The Zambezi Delta meets the needs of some 30 million people across many countries including Angola, Botswana, Malawi, Mozambique, Namibia, Zambia and Zimbabwe. Economic valuations have estimated the **total annual value of the Zambezi river-dependent ecosystem services to be between US$930 million and US$1.6 billion**. The net economic value of just the fisheries in four floodplain systems of the Zambezi Basin is estimated at US$16.4 million per annum, providing more than US$9.5 million in cash per annum to rural households. And the impact of changing hydrological regimes can be costly. The Zambezi River Basin has one of the most variable climates of any major river basin in the world, with an extreme range of conditions across the catchment and through time. The river flows have been modified by large dams, with more than 11% of the mean annual flow of the Zambezi evaporating from large reservoirs associated with hydropower dams.[6] During the severe 1991/92 drought, reduced hydropower generation resulted in an estimated US$102 million reduction in GDP in the Zambezi River Basin, a US$36 million reduction in export earnings and the loss of 3,000 jobs.[7]

The Luangwa floodplain is also vital locally: both culturally and economically. It supports local communities spread across 25 chiefdoms through provision of safe drinking water, floodplain agriculture, fishing, goods and trade, the wild fruit industry, honey, construction and craft materials. The Luangwa also has significant cultural and spiritual heritage for the country.[8] A rapid desktop analysis of direct use of Luangwa in 2001 valued the wetlands at over US$14 million per year; by far the greatest value was fisheries which made up just over half of this value (US$7million), followed by crops (US$4.5 million), natural products and medicine (US$2.3 million) and cattle (US$1.2 million) (US$ converted to 2019 values[9]).[10]

WWF is calling for the Luangwa to be protected as a Water Resource Protection Area under the Zambian 2011 Water Resources Management Act as dam developments are mooted.[1]

"Our chiefdom is one of the few chiefdoms that still have the natural habitat of our country. And it has one of Zambia's greatest rivers, the Luangwa. It gives them water. It gives them fish. It supports the wildlife around which the tourism economy is centred." **Senior Chief Luembe[2]**

© James Suter/Black Bean Productions/WWF

Sharing land between lions and livestock

The fates of lions are largely determined by the actions of resident or nomadic people living alongside them.[1] The extensive drylands of sub-Saharan Africa are vital for the livestock sector which provides over 10% of the region's GDP.[2] Grazing involves over 250 million pastoralists who live and move on 43% of Africa's landmass,[3] own a third of the region's livestock and supply 60% of the beef, 40% of other meat and 70% of the milk consumed.[4] Agricultural policies, land tenure trends and population increase have had major impacts on how pastoralism is practised across much of Africa, with more settled, intensive grazing becoming the norm.[5,6,7,8] Today, drylands face increasingly acute threats from the over-use of resources, an increase in cattle, poor management and a changing climate.

The most rapid declines in wildlife populations have occurred where there is both a predominance of pastoralism or agriculture and little financial value to be gained from wildlife.[9] Land competition and permanent settlement have exacerbated wild animal predation of livestock and people. Although not always the primary predator[10,11] or reason for livestock mortality,[12] lions are often killed when livestock is threatened.[13] However there are ways to encourage co-existence and ensure that the wider values of lions are maintained. Predator-proof enclosures, for example Living Walls, around bomas (livestock enclosure) are extremely cost effective methods to stop night-time lion attacks.[14,15] . The 'Lion-guardian' type approaches (see page 71), involving combinations of improved corralling of livestock, improved herding, the monitoring of lions to allow for warning of communities when they approach homesteads and the employment of respected locals to engage with local people around lion conservation issues are proving effective at reducing retaliatory killing of lions by pastoralists. Community-based conservation initiatives such as grazing plans that create spatial and temporal separation between wildlife and livestock have proven effective.[16,17] Compensation schemes are also available in some areas.[18] If top predators are to survive, policies and planning need to be developed which centre on co-existence.[19]

Kenya provides some good examples of integrating livestock production and wildlife conservation. Research, and often hundreds of years of reality, has clearly demonstrated that lions can survive outside of fenced areas within pastoral regions if communities gain benefits from wildlife.[20] In the Mara conservancies, lions have increased by between two to six-fold[21] and have likewise increased by about three-quarters in the Maasai group ranches and communal lands around Amboseli National Park.[22] The Olkiramatian and Shompole Group Ranches of Kenya's South Rift

If top predators are to survive, policies and planning need to be developed which centre on co-existence

region retain traditional methods of pastoralist livestock husbandry and demonstrate how to create a financially viable model of coexistence with carnivores outside of protected areas.[23,24, 25, 26] The area is the focus of the 'Rebuilding the Pride' lion conservation project.[27] As with other projects that encourage co-existence, such as the 'Linking Livestock Markets to Wildlife Conservation'[28] programme, the aim is to help grazers in arid areas to secure more reliable, higher margins for their livestock through access to established markets in return for conservation management. The programme is helping trade more than US$1 million worth of cattle annually and nearly 1,500 individual members from 10 different community conservancies are trading with the scheme.[29] Private or communal land with high wildlife conservation potential, such as land adjacent to national parks, is also the focus of leasing land for conservation programmes. Landowners in a land lease scheme are protecting an important part of a corridor between Amboseli National Park and Chyulu Hills in Kenya, and are paid directly in return for agreed restrictions on land use.[30] This is currently worth some US$240,000 per annum to local landowners in seven community conservancies. Tourism is one source of funding; within five years of start-up funding of US$50,000, the Tawi lodge[31] had leveraged around US$550,000 for communities leasing land in one conservancy in the corridor.[32]

Water, soil and productivity

Soils host the majority of the world's biodiversity and healthy soils are essential to securing food and fibre production. Ensuring the productivity of land, particularly in arid areas, is vital for the survival of many rural communities. The Food and Agricultural Organization of the United Nations (FAO) launched an Afrisoils programme in 2018 in recognition of the severe pressures facing Africa's soils.[1] Land degradation in sub-Saharan Africa is believed to be expanding rapidly, accompanied by the lowest agriculture and livestock yields in the world.

Africa has 33 million farms of less than two hectares, accounting for 80% of all farms,[2] although the trend towards larger, often foreign-owned plantations is increasing, including for biofuels.[3] Most land is still under informal title[4] making small farmers particularly vulnerable to land-grabbing and up to 55 per cent of the projected global expansion in agricultural land by 2050 is expected to occur in Africa and the Middle East.[5] Yet the land being brought under production is not always suited to agriculture and land degradation is increasing.[6] Furthermore, poorly planned water infrastructure projects can further undermine traditional pastoralist systems,[7] as can the conversion of grasslands to crops and other uses.[8] The loss of these ecosystem processes is impacting nutrient cycling and production[9] and poor soils increase water losses and impact productivity.[10]

Land degradation in sub-Saharan Africa is expanding rapidly

Protecting the most fragile habitats may be an important step in reducing erosion. Land degradation is a recognised national challenge in Ethiopia,[11] and protected areas are a tool to mitigate desertification. Alatash National Park was established in 2006 primarily to protect habitat from desertification[12] and is home to a hundred or more lions.[13] In other lion landsapes in Kenya and Tanzania, a Dutch NGO Justdiggit is implementing large-scale habitat restoration projects. 72,000 water harvesting bunds were constructed on Kuku Group Ranch, to stimulate revegetation, and communities are supported to set up grass seedbanks of species suitable for arid areas. In Amboseli National Park, the NGO is working on restoration of degraded areas in collaboration with local Maasai communities.[14]

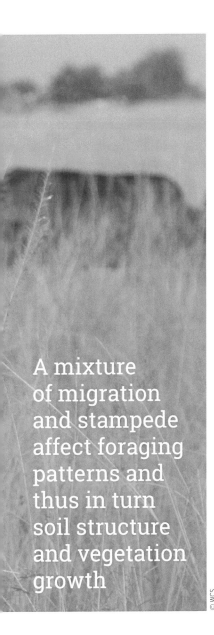

A mixture of migration and stampede affect foraging patterns and thus in turn soil structure and vegetation growth

© WCS

In Mali, Kenya, Ethiopia and numerous other African countries the livestock sector provides over 10% of GDP[15] and mobile livestock rearing is estimated to be between two and ten times more productive per unit of land than commercial ranching.[16] However, nearly three-quarters of the region's rangelands are degraded;[17] resulting in a loss of pastoral productivity.[18] Traditional livestock rearing systems that can be practised in fragile, arid and semi-natural ecosystems remain critically important for many people. Livestock rearing is still largely based on pastoralism, which if managed correctly can provide sustainable production in semi-natural areas.[19]

Much of the lion range is characterised by the mix of predator, scavenger and herbivore. Although there have been limited studies in the region, research in other biomes illustrates the regulatory role predators play in intact ecosystems limiting prey communities and thus reducing consumption of plant species important to humans.[20] The behaviour of wild herbivores evolved in response to predators like lions and the need to find food and water. A mixture of migration and stampede affected foraging patterns and thus in turn soil structure and vegetation growth.[21] Traditional pastoralists use herd mobility and species diversity (e.g. cattle, goats, etc.) to track grass biomass as they are made available by the rains.[22, 23] In this way, domestic herds mimic the behaviour of wild herbivores.[24]

Pastoralists often have elaborate customs and arrangements governing the use of water and pasture, enabling equitable communal resource use over vast areas and in some cases across international boundaries.[25] In Chad, for example, seasonal floods are a characteristic of the vast grasslands of Zakouma National Park and its surroundings making the area a stronghold for biodiversity, including lions,[26] and pastoralists, thanks to water availability throughout the year. Arabic transhumant herders from northern Chad move to the area during the dry season, however conservation planning has at times not considered the seasonal use rights of pastoralists nor involved them in management negotiations.[27,28]

Increasing cultivation and land privatisation, along with unsympathetic development policies and consequent loss of traditional cultures, are all major threats to pastoralism, increased by government policies leading many countries to prioritise more sedentary lifestyles.[29] As traditions fade away, tensions increase,[30,31] and, for example, in Central African Republic and northeast Democratic Republic of Congo armed pastoralists are actively involved in poaching and poison predators, such as lions.[32]

Forestry and non-timber forest products

What is left of the lion range in Africa tends to be in the drier savannah areas,[2] which do not have major potential for commercial timber production; these areas of Miombo and Mopane woodlands, however, support the livelihoods of 100 million rural people, a contribution estimated to be worth US$9 ± 2 billion/year.[3] Throughout the region, non-timber forest products (NTFPs) are important for example they are estimated to be worth US$7 million a year at 2007 prices in southern Africa,[4] and contributing approximately 20% to household income in poor communities.[5]

In Mozambique and parts of Tanzania, forest management can be an important ecosystem service that co-exists with lions and other biodiversity. However deforestation is rife. Mozambique has lost nearly 3 million hectares, some 10%, of its forests since 2000. This impacts ecosystem service provision and economic stability, given that forests contribute more than US$300 million to the country's GDP. In response, the government has developed policies focused on the processing of timber in Mozambique to increase local employment and value-added of forest products.[6]

There are, reassuringly, some good examples of forest management in Mozambique. In the late 1990s, the government received aid funding to assess the resource potential of the northern Sofala province in central-eastern Mozambique, with a view to establishing a major conservation area. The end result was the creation of a mix of hunting and timber concessions linking the Gorongosa National Park in the west with the Marromeu Special Reserve in the east. The primary aim was to create a conservation zone where the natural resources could be utilised sustainably and traditional game migration routes could be re-established without being restricted by fences.[7]

LevasFlor[8] has one of these concessions covering 46,000 ha of miombo woodlands. A successful and expanding venture,[9] the company's environmental and social credentials are recognised through Forest Stewardship Council (FSC) certification, the only one currently awarded in Mozambique.[10] As part of the requirement for certification, LevasFlor must protect wildlife in the concession and areas of forest with high conservation value (HCVF) are protected against all forms of utilisation.[11]

Miombo and Mopane woodlands support the livelihoods of 100 million rural people

"At LevasFlor we are very passionate about sustainability and the creation of jobs for local communities. The FSC certification is important to us as it demonstrates to customers, local government and other stakeholders about our commitment to the environment and will help us in accessing the overseas market."

Claudia Esteves, LevasFlor Sales and Compliance Manager[1]

© USAID Biodiversity & Forestry

Food and agriculture in lionscapes

The role of natural ecosystems in food security is increasingly recognised and the term 'biodiversity for food and agriculture' has become an important concept for institutions such as the FAO.[1] Critical elements relevant here are pollination services, the significance of crop wild relatives for crop breeding, the use of natural ecosystems directly for food resources and the more general role of healthy ecosystems in managing pests.[2]

Wildlife corridors and natural areas within farming districts therefore do not only support large species like lions, but also help to maintain essential ecosystem services for the farmer. Almost 90% of flowering plant species are pollinated by animals[3] and crops at least partially pollinated by animals produce 35% of global food.[4] Bees are the main pollinators,[5] along with other insects, birds and bats. Most farmers still rely on wild species and possibly bees from local beekeepers. Wild pollinators are important even where honey bees are abundant and are associated with higher crop yields;[6] diversity also helps to insure against a collapse in populations of individual pollinator species.[7] But pollinators everywhere are declining;[8] for instance, 16.5% of vertebrate pollinators are at risk of extinction.[9] Pollinators are affected by farm management practices,[10] and are supported by a mosaic of natural landscapes amongst farms, which will also contain predators of pests and other supportive wild species. **Studies of coffee pollination in Uganda found profitability strongly declined the further production was from natural habitats such as forest,** and valued pollination services for coffee crops established close to native forests at US$900/ha/year.[11] Bees also provide honey, and honey collection often overlaps with lion territories, for example in Malawi[12] and Ethiopia where beekeeping accounts for 1.3% of agricultural GDP.[13]

Natural ecosystems also still provide huge numbers of people with food, either regularly or as an emergency food store in times when agriculture fails. While over-collection remains an important pressure on many wild species, sustainable collection can go hand in hand with conservation. Where lions overlap with wetland areas, for instance, fisheries can provide a major source of food as in Malawi where Vwaza Marsh Wildlife Reserve provides over 5-6,000 kg of fish a year for local communities[14] and the Luangwa wetland in Zambia provides fisheries valued at over US$5 million a year.[15] Insects are also an important source of protein, minerals and vitamins, with some 250 edible species used in Africa. Research in the capital of the **Central African Republic estimated that 29% of the total annual consumption of animal proteins was obtained from caterpillars and larvae.**[16]

© Sue Stolton

Balanced ecosystems also help to control species that can disrupt agriculture. In West Africa, olive baboons (*Papio anubis*) increased in abundance at rates most closely correlated with declines in lion and leopards,[17] a phenomenon known as mesopredator release.[18] Baboon numbers can increase five-fold when predators are driven to extinction. In such numbers, they pose the greatest threat to crops and use many of the same sources of animal protein and plant foods as humans in sub-Saharan Africa. In some areas, baboon raids in agricultural fields require families to keep children out of school so they can help guard planted crops. **Restoration of top predators such as lions is thought to be the most effective way of controlling baboons.**[19]

A range of genetic variation is needed within crops to help them adapt to changing environmental conditions and to new pressures. Crop breeders draw on genetic material in traditional crop varieties (known as landraces) developed over millennia of farmer experimentation, and on genetic material from crop wild relatives (or CWR). CWR are either the wild species from which a crop was developed or a close relative, and have the potential to contribute beneficial traits to crops, such as pest or disease resistance, yield improvement or stability.[20] However, like other wild plant species they are exposed to a growing threat of extinction and loss of genetic diversity. Natural ecosystems are primary sources of CWR,[21] including particularly protected areas.[22] The lion range contains many areas with important CWR resources (see box for example), with one of the most important being wild coffee. There are 124 coffee species, the majority of which are found in Africa. Although about two-thirds of coffee species occur within at least one protected area, globally 60% of wild coffee species are threatened with extinction. Many coffee species in Africa overlap the lion range and many are also threatened, e.g. over 70% of wild coffee species in Tanzania are threatened.[23]

Protecting genetic variation useful for crop breeding within the lion range

Waza National Park, Cameroon, include the Yaéré floodplains containing wild rice (*Oryza barthii*) and Sorghum sp.;[24]

Bale Mountains National Park, Ethiopia, home to wild coffee[25] which has an estimated value of US$280/ha/yr[26] and other areas important for coffee are close to areas important for lions towards the border of Sudan;[27]

Aïr and Ténéré National Nature Reserve, Niger, harbours crop genetic resources of several important species: wild olive (*Olea europaea subsp. oleaster*), millet (*Pennisetum glaucum*), barley, wheat and sorghum (*S. aethiopicum*);[28]

Usambara Mountains East and West, Tanzania, two species of wild coffee have been identified;[29]

Kibale National Park, Uganda, wild robusta coffee (*Coffea canephora*) is found in the forest understorey.[30]

CASE STUDY:

Mopane worms, a source of funds and protein

Zambezian and Mopane Woodlands are dispersed throughout southern Africa, and much of the area remains a stronghold for lions.[2] The 'mopane worm' is one of the most economically important woodland resource products of the mopane tree (*Colophospermum mopane*). Not a worm at all, but the caterpillar of the moth *Imbrasia belina*, the worm is considered a delicacy and widely consumed by rural and, increasingly, urban populations across southern Africa.[3,4] The annual harvest may contribute up to a quarter of a household's cash income, depending on the quantity of mopane worms harvested, the proportion that is sold and the household's other sources of income.[5]

Despite the significant contribution of mopane wood and non-wood products, such as firewood and building material, to rural people's livelihoods, unsustainable harvesting is currently a widespread problem, with depletion especially severe around villages.[6] The value of mopane to human wellbeing has previously been overlooked in most conservation strategies and programmes.[7]

Mopane worms are important as both a local food source and for trade. People in Africa as a whole have the lowest protein intake per capita per day, particularly in rural areas, making the protein rich mopane worm a critically important food source. Trade of mopane worms is currently a commercial business in Zimbabwe, Botswana and South Africa. It has been estimated that the trade has the potential to create over 10,000 seasonal jobs across southern Africa.[8] A kilo of raw mopane worms is worth about US$1.40 in Namibia,[9] less than US$1 in Zimbabwe, and US$2.50-4.00 in

"With unemployment high, particularly in the rural communities outside the park around the harvesting area, this is another way for us to contribute towards the wellbeing and livelihoods of some of those families."

William Mabasa, Kruger National Park[1]

South Africa, where the estimated trade is worth from US$30 to US$50 million per year, of which some 40% goes to rural women. Trade is primarily regional, but the worm is also exported as far away as to the USA and South Korea.[10]

The increasing trade in mopane worms to supply the urban diet is however leading to overharvest in some places. **Traditional management practices are therefore important in lionscapes**, such as by the Uukwaluudhi traditional authority in Namibia[11] and the Kalanga of Bulilimamangwe District, Zimbabwe.[12] Kruger National Park in South Africa has also explored mopane worm harvesting in the Nxanatseni (northern) Region,[13] through the development of memorandums of understanding with local communities.[14]

Health from lionscapes

"The indigenous plant products industry in Namibia ... present rural communities with important income generating opportunities [and the] industry is significant for the national economy because of its growth potential."

National Botanical Research Institute, Namibia[1]

Over a quarter of all known plants have been used medicinally at some period.[2] Globally at least 60% of medicinal plants are gathered from the wild,[3] and the value of medicinal plants in the international marketplace is more than US$50 billion annually.[4] As land use change increases, it is not surprising that protected areas are often important sources of traditional medicines, which remain the primary health care option for up to 80% of the African population.[5] In Uganda, for example, more than 80% of the population depend on indigenous medicines that are less costly and more accessible than allopathic medicines.[6] Much of the lion range includes areas where the collection of medicinal plants is important for health, including Vwaza Marsh Wildlife Reserve in Malawi[7] and Bale National Park, Ethiopia. Observations and semi-structured interviews in the latter gathered data detailing how 56 ailments were managed, using 101 different ethnomedicinal plant species. Most of the medicinal plant species reported were threatened.[8]

A well-known example in the lion range is the trade in *Harpagophytum procumbens*,[9] part of the sesame family of plants and growing mainly in the Kalahari region of Namibia, Botswana and South Africa, Angola and to a lesser extent in Zambia, Zimbabwe and Mozambique;[10] an area that is also home to lions. The common name 'devil's claw' refers to the plant's hooked fruits. The tubers have been used for their medicinal properties since ancient times by indigenous people in Southern Africa. Traditional knowledge has been backed up by studies by the modern pharmaceutical industry, including some clinical trials, proving the efficacy of 'devil's claw' in treating rheumatoid arthritis and similar conditions. This has supported the increasing trade in dried devil's claw tubers. Harvesting is conducted by rural people, with between 10,000 and 15,000 harvesters relying on sales of dried tubers as their only source of income at the turn of the millennium.[11]

In Namibia, there are 8,000 producers involved in harvesting and processing indigenous plant products. Trade is dominated by devil's claw, making up 98% (over 540,000 kg) of estimated exports in 2012 and responsible for the majority of the N$100 million (US$6.9 million) income

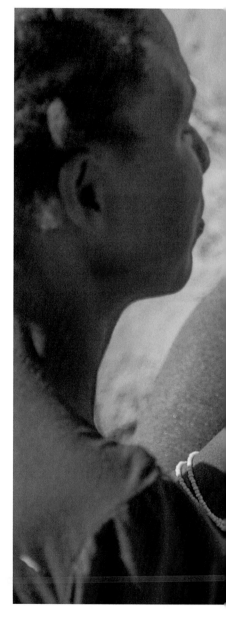

generated between 2009 and 2012.[12] Demand has led to over-collection and introduction of controlled harvesting through the issuing of permits.[13] In Bwabwata National Park, wild collection of devil's claw has achieved organic certification, through a collaborative project with WWF. Collectors, primarily women, in the Kyaramacan Association harvest only a third of the roots identified, once a year, and remove tubers from one side of the plant, stimulating growth in remaining tubers and ensuring sustainability.[14]

Much of the medical wisdom that has been developed over millennia is also now being used as the building blocks for the global pharmaceutical trade through bioprospecting, the search for wild species that contain chemicals with potential medicinal or commercial applications. Ethnobotanical knowledge is being studied by research institutes to see if it can be adapted for use in 'western medicine'; for instance the US National Cancer Institute spent nearly US$89 million in 2004 in studying a range of traditional therapies.[15] Interest waned a little in the first decade of the 21st century but has now increased again,[16] although it should be noted that such activities can raise questions about who owns the knowledge.[17] Examples of bioprospecting in the lion range include Manovo-Gounda-St. Floris National Park, Central African Republic, where a possible anti-HIV compound was isolated from *Chrysobalanus icaco* subsp. *Atacorensis*[18] and Etosha National Park in Namibia where a compound with antimicrobial and fungicidal properties, which could be used for controlling fungal infections in humans, was discovered.[19]

It is also important to consider the negative effects of environmental degradation. For example, a decline in top predators such as lions has led to an expansion in the olive baboon in Ghana. Baboons and humans share many pathogens and parasites, so that increased interactions have led to an increase in intestinal parasites in human communities.[20] In Malawi and Mozambique, woodland degradation, as evidenced by decreasing resource availability (e.g. scarcity of both fuelwood and medicinal plants), has been observed in communities where HIV prevalence is high.[21] And the concept of 'ecological grief' as a response to ecological loss has been noted in the literature.[22]

In Namibia, there are 8,000 producers involved in harvesting and processing indigenous plant products for health

© Gareth Bentley/WWF-US

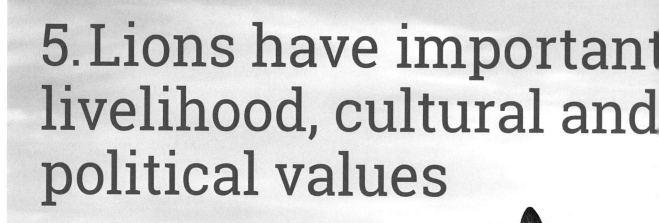

5. Lions have important livelihood, cultural and political values

"*This [Kenyan] heritage of diverse landscapes, essential ecosystem services and natural resources is the foundation of our collective development – both now and into the future.*"

Hon. Najib Balala, EGH, Cabinet Secretary, Ministry of Tourism & Wildlife, Kenya[1]

Symbols of indigenous cultures

"Long ago, they knew the secret of how men become lions when they die ... The tradition of transforming into a lion had its own secrets, and the 'nyakwawas', or chiefs of Mbire, knew it"

told by **Eugenio Almeda Canda, Chief of Canda, Mozambique**[2]

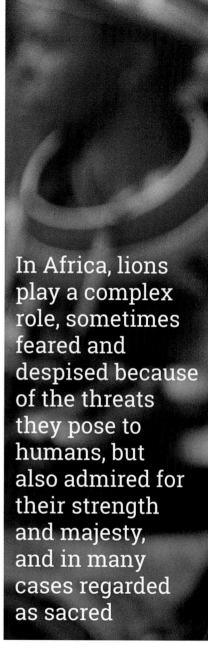

In Africa, lions play a complex role, sometimes feared and despised because of the threats they pose to humans, but also admired for their strength and majesty, and in many cases regarded as sacred

Lions have played a powerful role in human culture for tens of thousands of years. The earliest known depiction of a now-extinct lion ancestor is the Löwenmensch figurine. This 40,000 year-old 'lion-man' is one of the oldest-known animal-shaped sculptures and examples of figurative art in the world.[3] Cave paintings of lions can be found in Lascaux, France, dating from 32,000 to 15,000 years ago.[4] From 3,500 BCE, Egyptians were including lions amongst the pantheon of gods and on tomb paintings. Their war goddess Sekhmet, a lioness, was the protector of the pharaohs and responsible for the annual flooding of the Nile[5] and lion cults existed with mummified lion remains found in tombs.[6] The lion was a symbol of kinship in Mesopotamia; the goddess Inanna is often pictured standing on the backs of two lions[7] and later, worshipped under the name of Ishtar by the Babylonians and Assyrians, she is depicted with her chariot drawn by seven lions.[8] Lion carvings guarded city gates in Greece, Mycenae and the Hittite cities. In Iranian mythology, the lion is the symbol of courage and monarchy. These links pass over into the Christian tradition with Mark the Evangelist, author of the second gospel, symbolised by a lion, which is also the emblem of the tribe of Judah. For Jews, the lion is the symbol of messianic hope.

In Africa, lions play a complex role, sometimes feared and despised because of the threats they pose to humans, but also admired for their strength and majesty, and in many cases regarded as sacred. Lions are sacred to clans within the Ikoma tribe in western Serengeti for instance,[9] and the Tsonga and Sepedi people of South Africa venerate white lions as 'star beings' radiating a power of love and wisdom that keeps the soul of Africa alive.[10] The lion is a totemic animal for the Shona people in Zimbabwe.[11] Men were believed to be transformed into lions after death in parts of Mozambique.[12] In the highlands of Ethiopia, problems like livestock predation by lions are more likely to be tolerated due to the high cultural values of lions.[13] Conversely, lion killing also has cultural significance in many areas, bringing social status, attracting gifts from cattle herders in thanks and facilitating marriages, so that lion killing can sometimes persist even in the near-absence of livestock attacks.[14]

The Maasai, Samburu, Barabaig Wasukuma and other tribal groups in Kenya and Tanzania illustrate the complicated relationship between local people and lions. Traditionally, killing lions has formed an important part of initiation for young men,[15] with motivations for killing a mixture of culture and retaliation.[16] Reducing the level of killing therefore requires addressing both issues simultaneously. In the Amboseli ecosystem, attempts to reduce the rate of spearing and poisoning have focused on both compensation agreements and programmes that draw on traditional cultural values to inspire a conservation ethic, and in combination the two approaches have been extremely successful.[17] Across many areas within the lion range, young warriors are being trained to be 'Lion-guardians'[18,19,20,21,22] to monitor and protect lions; appreciating the species that was a traditional foe.[23] Yet cultural values are also changing; experience in both Kenya and Tanzania found that Christian, particularly evangelical, Maasai were more likely to kill lions,[24] suggesting that conservation efforts will need to continue to evolve. One innovative initiative is the Maasai Olympics, where killing lions is replaced by competitive sports based upon traditional warrior skills.[25] Similar complexity affects other cultural relationships with lions. The Sukuma people of Tanzania have traditionally paid lion killers to hunt lions that have destroyed cattle. This practice is continuing even though cattle losses are now negligible, although there are indications that such cultural practices are changing.[26]

Outside the lion range, lions hold huge cultural value, both inside and outside Africa. The killing of Cecil, a well-known lion in Zimbabwe, produced the largest global reaction in the history of nature conservation.[27,28]

Experiencing lions in nature

A tourism industry based mainly on foreign visitors contains many dangers; of elitism, risks from the vagaries of the market and criticisms due to the climate implications of air travel. As countries become urbanised, people's relationship with nature changes, on the one hand becoming less intense but also often developing new interests in wildlife for its own sake. Domestic tourism is a critical step in building long-term interest in and support for lions and other wildlife in Africa, and understanding the associated ecosystem services is a critical step in this process. Initiatives such as the Wildlife Clubs of Kenya, which has involved over a million children,[1] provide useful models that other countries could follow. Online tools provide easy access to a growing number of people. For example, National Geographic's Lion Crittercam simulation game[2] helps students to learn how to study large carnivore populations, while Zooniverse encourages users to help in identifying game photographed in camera traps, for example in Serengeti,[3] as does the Zoological Society of London's Instant Wild app which relays live images of wildlife from cameras around the world, including for example Lewa Conservancy in Kenya.[4]

At a time when many African children will have little direct exposure to nature, protected and conserved areas become vital links with the natural world. Some projects are leading the way: for example, WildlifeDirect takes children between eight and 12 years old to the national parks and reserves throughout Kenya aiming to create a generation of Wildlife Warriors; young advocates and champions of conservation;[5] and Ewaso Lions Lion Kids Camp programme aims to inspire a new generation of conservationists through a combination of education, safaris, games and activities.[6]

The Kenyan government has a specific goal to cultivate "*national pride, public support and active engagement of all Kenyans in the conservation of this rich national heritage and natural asset*".[7] Domestic visitors make up about 64% of tourist numbers in Nairobi National Park,[8] but local visitation still remains relatively low and poor marketing is identified as one of the reasons, alongside lack of disposable income and the high cost of food inside national parks.[9] However, things can change very quickly and both government and privately protected areas should be planning for an upsurge in local visits. A generation ago, South Korea had an economy similar to many of the poorer African countries and a mainly rural population; today it has largely urbanised but also developed a major domestic tourism base in protected areas. Thirty-eight million people visited South Korea's national parks in 2007, around 99% of whom were domestic visitors.[10]

At a time when many African children will have little direct exposure to nature, protected and conserved areas become vital links with the natural world

Lions as icons

The lion is a symbol of Africa and an immensely powerful icon in the modern world. Images of animals are 'copyright free' meaning that companies and organisations do not need to pay a fee to use lions for their branding.[1] Lions feature in the logo of literally hundreds of companies, including famous brands like MGM film studios, Peugeot and Saab cars, Cunard Liners, the Royal Bank of Canada, Lowenbrau beer and Lonsdale sporting manufacturers. 'The Lion's Share' is an effort to re-balance this wildlife branding issue.[2] The initiative is asking major advertisers to contribute 0.5% of their media buy for each campaign featuring an animal, with the fund aiming to raise US$100 million over the next three years, to be invested in species conservation. Supported by the United Nations Development Programme (UNDP), the initiative already has a number of large companies on board.[3]

Many sports use the lion as a symbol of power and strength, including the English Premier League, the England male and female football teams, the England and Wales Cricket Board and South African rugby team. In Africa, three national football teams are nicknamed after a lion: the Lions of the Atlas in Morocco, Les Lions Indomptables (The Indomitable Lions or Untameable Lions) in Cameroon and the Lions of Teranga in Senegal (*teranga* being a Wolof word referring to hospitality and deeply symbolic in the country). It is ironic that lions are extinct in Morocco, confined to Bénoué National Park and Waza National Park in Cameroon, found only (and in very low numbers) in Niokolo-Koba National Park in Senegal and listed as Critically Endangered throughout west and central Africa on the IUCN Red List.[4]

The lion is the national animal in:

African countries with lions: Ethiopia, Gambia, Kenya, Liberia and Togo

African and Middle East countries that used to have lions: Morocco, Iran and Libya (extinct Barbary lion)

Many other countries around the world: Armenia, Belgium, Bulgaria, England, Luxembourg, Netherlands, Singapore and Sri Lanka

Building pride for lions

By inspiring tolerance, respect and pride for lions, as well as an increasing awareness of new legislation, the Lilongwe Wildlife Trust (LWT) in Malawi aims to reduce human-lion conflict and deter people from trading in carnivore products and bushmeat. The 'twin-track' campaign is designed to target a range of audiences from law enforcers and the media through to rural communities around protected areas and urban consumers of bushmeat. Activities include producing a song on lions performed by a leading Malawian artist, an animation and short films on the 'pride of Malawi' and the law relating to

bushmeat. An educational and media outreach programme includes a 'pedal power' cinema reaching communities without electricity and World Lion Day community rallies. The campaign will also complement LWT's work on the government's wildlife justice programme, which has achieved some significant successes combatting organised wildlife criminals who are known to trade in bushmeat and carnivore parts. Stamping out these trades is critical for the protection of lions in Malawi, where populations are on the rise in large part thanks to re-introductions by African Parks Network.

Improving security across lionscapes

Security of environmental resources and human security are inextricably linked.[2] Law enforcement, particularly in areas of political instability, can be an important contributor to local and regional security.[3] In areas where government institutions are failing, protected area managers and rangers sometimes provide a framework of much-needed stability.[4] One of the motivating factors for local people to form the conservancies of northern Kenya has been the fact that they lead to improved security and reduced cattle theft.[5]

Since 2013, a security crisis has been unravelling the social fabric of the Central African Republic.[6] More than a dozen armed groups and a multitude of local militias have usurped control of about 80% of the country. Chinko, a 50-year public-private partnership that includes the Central African Republic's Environment Ministry, USAID, the African Parks Network[7] and the Walton Family Foundation, is bringing some element of security to nearly 1.8 million hectares of the country.[8] Chinko is the largest employer in the region, some 400 local people, and is by far the largest taxpayer in Eastern CAR. Additionally, dozens of nurses and teachers are funded by the park. In 2017, 380 Internally Displaced People, mainly women and children, fled to Chinko seeking sanctuary from civil unrest and were protected by the park and rangers.[9] In restoring security, Chinko has become a primary source of stability and safety for an entire region. Lions are also finding a safe haven in the park.[10]

But without proper resourcing of protected area management, the situation can be reversed. Waza National Park in Cameroon is a less encouraging example of what can happen during a period of insecurity. The Waza region suffers from terrorism through groups such as Boko Haram. Lack of management resources has led to the park becoming a refuge for both bandits and poachers. As one local villager observed *"If the park guards were here they would be able to protect the park"*.[11] More

"A strong kernel of law enforcement can have a big impact on a larger region of anarchy .... we're here for conservation – but when no one else is around, everyone looks to you for help."

David Simpson, Chinko Park Manager[1]

recently, in remote areas with fewer resources to steal, the park has become a refuge for pastoralists seeking to escape violence. Law enforcement associated with the protected area would in this case be welcomed by local people.[12] The park still has a population of lions.[13]

Several countries within the lion range are in situations of such political insecurity that investment in protected areas can help foster national and regional security; for example in Zakouma National Park in Chad,[14] and Garamba National Park in the Democratic Republic of Congo.[15] Strengthening management in protected areas that cross national borders, or where protected areas meet at a border, can also sometimes help improve regional security,[16] including, for example, around Uganda, between Sudan and South Sudan, Ethiopia and Eritrea, Chad, CAR, Nigeria and Cameroon.

Dinka seasonal cattle camp, Sudan, with the cows waiting to be taken out for grazing.

© Peter Lindsey

6. Lions can generate economic benefits and attract new sources of revenue

"Payments for Ecosystem Services ... has the potential to help raise new sources of sustainable finance where they are greatly lacking and improve the efficiency of conservation interventions, which has been said to be low in Africa."

African Development Bank Group[1]

© Ed Selfe

What kind of economy do we want?

"If Africa loses its lions and other iconic wildlife species it will lose out on one of the major competitive edges that it has over other regions of the world."

Peter Lindsey, Director, Lion Recovery Fund, Wildlife Conservation Network[2]

The International Monetary Fund projects that Africa as a whole will be the world's second-fastest growing economy to 2020. Most sub-Saharan African countries are experiencing annual GDP growth of over 5%,[3] coupled with rapid population growth and urbanisation. In 1960, there were five cities in sub-Saharan Africa with over half a million inhabitants; by 2015 this had increased to 84, by 2030 there will probably be over 140.[4] Africa's urban population is projected to be 1.23 billion by 2050,[5] with a twelve-fold increase in urban land cover.[6] Africa is also a major agricultural frontier. The African Development Bank Group reports that 70 million hectares of new arable land will be needed to feed the global population in 2050 and that 65% of this could be in sub-Saharan Africa.[7] The ADB will invest US$24 billion in agriculture and agribusiness over the next 10 years.[8] Colossal transport infrastructure development is also underway.[9,10] The influence of these massive developments on safeguarding wild lion populations in Africa has rarely been examined.

No-one is denying that Africa needs development. Many people are desperately poor, malnourished and lacking the infrastructure necessary for human wellbeing,[11] such as clean water.[12] But the type of development is critical. **Development that undermines basic ecosystem services will rebound on the very societies it is trying to support**. Talk of bringing new land into agriculture needs to be put into the context that 60% of current agricultural land is already degraded.[13] Woodfuel supplies over 80% of household fuel in Africa, creating deforestation problems and health risks; household air pollution from biomass caused more deaths than malaria in 2010 and the death-rate is rising.[14] Not all the people investing in development recognise or care about these risks. Few African countries have a rigorous cost/benefit analysis of ecosystem services; their value is often only recognised in retrospect, once they have disappeared.

The lion should not only be a much used metaphor of rapidly developing economies but also — and perhaps more fundamentally — of a landscape approach that balances economic priorities and environmental safeguards and considers human needs together with those of other species. Lions' wide-ranging ecology, reliance on large prey species and intersection with global trade networks make them the perfect focus for national and cross-border cooperation for effective conservation action.[15] **New lion economies will be those that allow economic growth to exist alongside healthy populations of lions.**

Conservation management is not just about biodiversity, important though this is, but about the multiplicity of practical benefits that ecosystems provide related to food and water security, disaster risk reduction and climate adaptation. As we have shown, lionscapes contain a lot more than lions.

There are signs that this is being recognised. The African Development Fund has a target of using 40% of total annual approvals to promote climate-resilient and low-carbon development in Africa.[16] In June 2018, the Government of Kenya published its *National Wildlife Strategy 2030*; this contains four core Pillars and a set of underlying Goals, the first of the pillars is: *"Maintain and Improve Habitat and Ecosystem Integrity to reduce biodiversity loss, protect ecosystem function, enhance connectivity and increase resilience."*[17] And the Revealing Benin project (see page 88) also makes these links.[18] The Sustainable Development Goals, supported by all sub-Saharan African governments, include many that relate directly to lionscapes and their wider values (see page 19).

> Lions should not only be a metaphor of rapidly developing economies but also of a landscape approach that balances economic priorities and environmental safeguards

© Brent Stapelkamp

The challenge of creating the new lion economy

"We need to bring credible evidence, across all government sectors and non-state actors, that spending on biodiversity is actually a worthwhile investment."

Cristiana Pasca Palmer, Executive Secretary of the Convention on Biological Diversity[1]

© Donovan Jooste

Although the benefits from healthy ecosystems far surpass the proportion that can be valued economically,[2,3] there are important reasons for trying to understand the economic benefits from lionscapes. The value of many ecosystem services are overlooked – either ignored or seen as free services to society, which require no investment in management.[4] Many of these benefits are intangible – making them hard to measure. Even those ecosystem services that do lend themselves to economic valuation often present challenges to economists. The whole concept of ecosystem services is only just beginning to be understood, with methods for measurement varying and sometimes attempts to monetise values suggesting vastly different economic values, some of which may be hard to realise.[5,6]

As a consequence, investment in conservation, although increasingly needed to preserve intact ecosystems, is inadequate. The world at large benefits from the presence and existence value of lions but local people tend to bear most of the costs. At the same time, governments tend not to apportion sufficient value to wildlife.

The relationship between values and benefits from ecosystem services

Understanding how values flow from ecosystem services and who benefits from them has led to the development of a classification system based around three concepts: direct use, indirect use and non-use/future use.

Direct use values refer to immediate uses we make of ecosystem services and are primarily provisioning services. It is relatively easy to understand direct use values and to assign them with socio-economic values. These values will likely have immediate benefits for surrounding communities.

Indirect use values come in more diffuse form, often affecting a large number of people, which sometimes include populations far from the origin of the value. They tend to be non-consumptive values and are often regulating services. Indirect use values could, for instance, be benefits such as clean water from a watershed or disaster risk reduction from soil stabilisation. Although indirect use values have important economic and welfare consequences, it is sometimes difficult to assign them with accurate economic values and more difficult still to link with particular beneficiaries. Ecosystem services often only get recognised when they disappear.

Non-use values and/or options for future use refer to leaving a natural species or ecosystem in place even when we are not benefitting immediately from its existence. Several categories exist, including: **option values,** which relate to maintaining an area in case it may be needed for its natural resources in the future; **bequest values** of leaving things in place for future generations; and **existence values** that we consider important even though we do not benefit ourselves. The extent to which people understand and respond to non-use values varies dramatically; some individuals and some cultures understand and accept these wider reasons for protection, others find them much more difficult to comprehend or to take seriously.

Options for turning benefits from lions into financial value

At present successful conservation is being provided by a much undervalued group of people including indigenous peoples, local communities, conservation professionals and passionate volunteers from around the world. Few other services, apart perhaps from the equally underfunded healthcare sector, are so reliant on the goodwill of the service providers. **It has been estimated that effective management of a protected area in the lion range needs funding of around US$1,000 to US$2,000 per km^2 or between US$1.2 to US$2.4 billion annually.**[1] (To put this into perspective, the upper figure equals the duty free sales at Incheon Airport in South Korea in 2018[2]) But current funding is far below this, with lion range protected areas only receiving about US$381 million annually, or around US$200/km^2.[3] The lion range outside of these areas receives even less, with 80% of financing from temporary or donor sources,[4] and investments are needed to help safeguard sustainable management in conservancies and other land use options where wildlife and humans can coexist and a full range of ecosystem services flourish.

One of the best chances of ensuring effective conservation depends upon translating the global value of iconic species such as lions into tangible local benefits large enough to drive conservation across the lion range.[5] A few countries in Africa, such as Tanzania, Kenya, Botswana, Namibia and South Africa, clearly demonstrate that investment in wildlife conservation leads to major tourism benefits. Others like Malawi, Benin and Rwanda are also starting to re-access tourism dollars following policies that support conservation and tourism. But many other **countries, such as Mozambique, Ethiopia, Zambia, Angola and several countries in West and Central Africa, run the risk of losing their wildlife without ever really having benefitted from it in terms of tourism dollars.**

Funding for lion conservation that also safeguards ecosystem services can come from a variety of sources. And sites can benefit from a range of complementary services; for example the Chyulu Hills in Kenya runs a REDD+, has a water PES scheme being set up, as well as a land lease scheme and livestock compensation programme. However, where financial mechanisms are put in place, it is important that benefits are balanced across communities. All too often, wildlife's economic benefits are captured at national or international levels, whilst the cost of living with wildlife (e.g. human–wildlife conflict) is mostly felt at the local level.[6,7]

It is important that benefits are balanced across communities. All too often, wildlife's economic benefits are captured at national or international levels, whilst the cost of living with wildlife (e.g. human–wildlife conflict) is mostly felt at the local level.

© UN Photo/P Mugabane

Some of the more well-known options for funding which can be linked to ecosystem service delivery are discussed below – whilst other options such as bioprospecting, natural capital bonds, etc. have yet to realise their potential.[8]

Direct finance

- Leases (a contractual arrangement where the lessee (user) pays the lessor (owner) for use of an asset) in return for conservation actions: e.g. the land lease scheme to create a conservation corridor between Amboseli National Park and Chyulu Hills in Kenya (see page 55) and the leasing of management rights of protected areas to philanthropists/ NGOs: e.g. the Chinko in the Central African Republic (see page 76). However, leases (and concessions) are often not for sufficient periods of time to warrant large-scale investments.
- Concession (a contractual right to carry on a certain kind of business or activity in an area) where operators pay funds to run activities in areas owned by another entity, such as government protected areas and community conservancies: e.g. the W-Arly Pendjari ecosystem in Benin, Burkina Faso and Niger where private operators have management responsibilities in return for hunting rights (see page 88).
- Entry fees or conservation taxes usually related to tourism operations: fees vary widely but are a major contribution to management and local development costs in many countries.[9]
- Payment for Ecosystem Services: donors have pledged US$5 billion for carbon related services around the world[10] (see page 42) and total watershed payments are conservatively estimated to exceed US$50 billion to date (over US$9.3 billion annually).[11] Preparatory studies for the development of PES schemes across Africa have repeatedly demonstrated the willingness of beneficiaries to make payments for ecosystem services, however only a few PES schemes have been developed effectively to date.[12]
- Tax income: successful businesses paying taxes are the backbone of national economies. Tourism, in particular, is a major contributor to GDP for some countries and a rare contributor to the public purse in others; for example, the Chinko is the largest taxpayer in Eastern Central African Republic.[13]
- Offset markets: where a 'polluter' pays for the negative impact they impose on the environment by purchasing credits or offsets, for example through the voluntary forest carbon market (see page 44) or biodiversity offsets. Globally the forest carbon markets raised over US$170 million in 2010 and could generate US$7 billion by 2020; whilst biodiversity offsets raised well over US$2 billion in 2010 and could generate nearly US$ 10 billion in 2020.[14]

Indirect finance

Debt-for-nature swaps or debt-for-development swaps can provide public or private finance through a cancellation or restructuring of debt. A creditor, e.g. a government of a donor country, can agree to cancel debts under the condition that the debtor (e.g. a country) reinvests the equivalent amount into initiatives for sustainable development. Alternatively, debt can be restructured rather than cancelled (for example through lower interest rates). The freed capital from this restructuring of debt can then be invested in conservation and sustainable development.[15,16] There are some highly-indebted countries across the lion range where 'debt-for-nature' schemes have particular potential, for example Zimbabwe, Nigeria, Angola, Sudan, Somalia and Cameroon.

Avoided losses

Economic sustainability across the lion range is also impacted by a range of issues leading to environmental degradation.

- In many countries, investments in built infrastructure tend to be more attractive politically than investments in natural infrastructure, despite the latter offering substantial ecological and socio-economic benefits.[17] There needs to be a re-focus on ecological infrastructure, based around naturally-functioning ecosystems that deliver valuable services to people, providing a nature-based equivalent to built infrastructure.[18] For example, in South Africa the Addo Elephant National Park has increased vegetation cover improving water infiltration, reducing soil erosion and increasing carbon sequestration (see page 40).
- Tourism is already a major source of finance for countries across the lion range. Economic losses from poaching in protected areas in Malawi have been conservatively estimated to cost the country around US$6 million each year (see page 24).[19]
- Carbon emissions from land-use change in Africa are significant and, unlike the rest of the world, are higher than the fossil fuel emissions.[20] Halting deforestation and degradation will thus reduce carbon emissions and, if planned effectively, deliver a wide range of additional benefits. For example, the Lion Carbon scheme in Zambia aims to protect ten million hectares of forest over a ten-year period while helping improve the livelihoods of a million people (see page 46).

CASE STUDY:

Revealing Benin

Revealing Benin is a large-scale investment programme from 2016-2021 based on 45 major projects across nine key sectors, which aim for a sustainable revitalisation of the country's economy. The programme has an initial budget of over US$15 million and aims to raise investment equal to 34% of GDP through collaboration with private sector partners, which will provide over 60% of the programme's total planned investment.[2]

One of the flagship projects of Revealing Benin is to make Pendjari National Park into one of West Africa's richest wildlife reserves. Pendjari is part of the W – Arly – Pendjari transnational complex (shared with the Republic of Niger and Burkina Faso), a UNESCO World Heritage site, one of the last wild landscapes in West Africa and home to a significant population of lions.[3] The government intends to transform it into the region's leading wildlife protected area, where visitors will be able to see the 'Big 5' in a range of luxury- and eco-tourism ventures. The aim for a roughly 50:50 private-public partnership to raise over US$50 million to invest in the park has led to the National Geographic Society, African Parks and the Wyss Foundation announcing a partnership to invest over US$23 million into the park's conservation.[4] The projected impacts will include 6,000 jobs and over US$25 million in export earnings.[5]

"...my government is committed to making tourism a lever for long-term development. It is all at once a matter of preservation of our environment and our natural resources, sustainable tourism and social impact."

Patrice Talon, President of the Republic of Benin[1]

© OeBenin

Conclusions: optimising ecosystem services from lionscapes

This report shows that the **lion range countries have a vast range of benefits associated with intact, healthy ecosystems.** But each country and region will have a range of different ecosystem services. Ensuring the effective management of these services, and where applicable, turning these services into effective conservation funding mechanisms and sustainable use will require specific jurisdictional approaches, e.g. at national, regional or sub-regional levels.

If Africa is to support a rapidly expanding human population and a growing economy, it needs to invest in ecosystem services as essential life-support mechanisms. A range of actions are needed.

If Africa is to support a rapidly expanding human population and a growing economy, it needs to invest in ecosystem services as essential life-support mechanisms

© Peter Lindsey

Measure and relay the value of ecosystem services (actual and potential) to all sectors of society: a report like this is just the start. Individual countries, and individual protected areas, need to understand and communicate the wider values that they contain.

Rebuild ecosystem services to improve food, water and human security in sub-Saharan Africa: many of these services have declined catastrophically, with impacts on humans and the rest of nature. Restoration is now a critical need throughout large parts of the continent.

Use the market for these ecosystem services to support conservation throughout the lion range: this means building carbon markets, and refining and applying PES schemes alongside ecotourism, trophy hunting and other current economic models.

Encourage policy makers to consider these benefits (and their potential loss): for example in delivery of the Sustainable Development Goals, Land Degradation Neutrality, the UNFCCC's land use change targets and the post-2020 biodiversity targets.

Create business models that support both ecosystem services and lions: working with companies to understand and implement practical responses.

Create conservation models that reflect the needs of human communities: using participatory approaches to work with communities to ensure fair distribution of any ecosystem service benefits.

Encourage governments and international donors to invest in lion conservation: including talking with those parts of the funding cycle who do not generally consider pure conservation projects.

Recognise the significance of the continent's unique biodiversity in shaping and sustaining Africa's cultural heritage: building support within and outside the continent.

Restore lion populations as an indicator of healthy ecosystem services.

7. End pieces

Declarations to Recover Lions

In May 2019, Disney Conservation Fund supported the Wildlife Conservation Network (WCN) to convene a gathering of more than 80 leading conservation experts at the Lion Footprint Forum. This meeting was the first of its kind and aimed at expanding collaboration to grow conservation impact. Over 55 field-based practitioners and 15 philanthropists were in attendance from 16 countries and representing more than 50 organizations and foundations. They discussed practical challenges and opportunities in lion conservation efforts and identified areas of collaboration to elevate the collective effort to save the species. One of the major outcomes of the meeting was the "Declarations to Recover Lions" which aspires to galvanize the conservation community around a succinct suite of strategies as a united front for halting the lion crisis.

Declarations to Recover Lions

We agree lions are in crisis and half the lions have been lost in the past 25 years with as few as 20,000 remaining in Africa. **Our shared commitment** is to ensure that wild lions, landscapes and African people thrive.

We recognise that the presidents and leaders of the African countries, and the communities who live alongside lions, are the custodians of African lions for the world.

We recognise that lions are national and global treasures.

We know that recovering lion populations is possible.

We work to:

Stop the loss
We must protect lions, their prey and their landscapes.

Reduce the cost
We must minimise the burden on people in Africa who share landscapes with lions.

Unlock the value
We must uncover and magnify the cultural, economic and ecological benefits lions and their landscapes bring to communities, national economies and the global community.

Acknowledgements

Firstly, we would like to thank Peter Lindsey and Paul Thomson of the Lion Recovery Fund for funding, supporting and commenting on this report. We would also like to thank Jeffrey (Jefe) Parrish for his help in developing the initial concept. Background research for the report included a study by Sophia Burke (AmbioTEK Community Interest Company) and Mark Mulligan and Claudia Gutierrez (King's College London) using the Co$ting Nature tool (http://www.policysupport.org/costingnature).

Many people were involved in providing initial information, support, inspiration, critical analysis and detailed comments. These include: Nikhil K. Advani, World Wildlife Fund US; Antony Alexander, Peace Parks Foundation Andrea Athanas, African Wildlife Foundation; John Baker, WildAid; Marc Baker, Carbon Tanzania; Hans Bauer, Wildlife Conservation Research Unit (WildCRU); Colleen. M. Begg, Niassa Carnivore Project; Shivani Bhalla, Ewaso Lions; Paola Bouley, Parque Nacional da Gorongosa; Greg Carr, Parque Nacional da Gorongosa; Krissie Clarke, PAMS Foundation; Jenny Cousins, WWF UK; Alayne Oriol Cotterill, Lion Landscapes; Tracey Cumming, Biodiversity Finance Initiative; Tim R.B. Davenport, Wildlife Conservation Society; Sarah Davies, Wildlife Crime Prevention; Amy Dickman, Wildlife Conservation Research Unit (WildCRU); Richard W. Diggle, WWF Namibia; Moussa Sega Diop, Senegal; Joanne Dube, African Parks; Neil Fitt, Kalahari Conservation Society; Angela Gaylard, African Parks; Elizabeth Greengrass, The Born Free Foundation; Jeremy Goss, Big Life Foundation; Elaine Hake, Lilongwe Wildlife Trust; Lise Hanssen, Kwando Carnivore Project; Peter Howard, Nairobi; Charlotte Karibuhoye, MAVA Foundation West Africa Programme; Laly Lichtenfeld, African People & Wildlife; Delphine Malleret King, The Long Run; Geoffroy Mauvais, IUCN African Protected Areas & Conservation; Michel Masozera, WWF International; Angus Middleton, Namibia Nature Foundation; Kate Moore, Lilongwe Wildlife Trust; Lana Muller, The Cape Leopard Trust; Philip Muruthi, African Wildlife Foundation; Musonda Mumba, UN Environment; Paul Ndiaye, École Polytechnique Fédérale de Lausanne; Fred Nelson, Maliasili; Leo Niskanen, IUCN, Nairobi; Ashley Robson; Fiona Paumgarten, University of the Witwatersrand – Johannesburg; Kaddu Sebunya, Africa Wildlife Foundation; Sue Snyman, IUCN Eastern and Southern Africa Regional Office; Marc Stalmans, Parque Nacional da Gorongosa; Franziska Steinbruch, Niassa National Reserve; Ian Stevenson, Conservation Lower Zambezi; Hannah Timmins; John Waithaka, IUCN World Commission on Protected Areas and Kenya Wildlife Service; Chris Weaver, WWF Namibia and Guy Western, South Rift Association of Landowners (SORALO).

We would also like to thank Caroline Snow for proof reading the report and Jonathan Gledson and Helen Miller for their excellent design. Despite all this help, any errors remain our own.

References and notes

PAGES 4-9

[1] https://timconwild.wordpress.com/2014/01/28/117/ (accessed 10/11/2018).

[2] Hon. Pohamba Shifeta, Minister of Environment and Tourism, MP, Namibia. Welcoming remarks at the occasion of the High Level Briefing Session on Biodiversity Finance 6th August 2018, Avani Hotel, Windhoek, https://resmob.org/wp-content/uploads/2018/09/Hon.-Shifeta-Welcoming-Remarks-Biodiversity-Economy.pdf (accessed 9/10/2018).

[3] The Liberalizing Innovation Opportunity Nations (LIONS@FRICA) partnership seeks ... to encourage and enhance Africa's innovation ecosystem and to spur entrepreneurship across the continent. https://www.afdb.org/en/news-and-events/lions-frica-partnership-to-promote-african-innovation-and-entrepreneurship-9211/ (accessed 25/10/2018).

[4] https://www.afdb.org/en/news-and-events/pride-of-african-lions-steer-post-mdg-agenda-afdb-president-donald-kaberuka-11459/ (accessed 25/10/2018).

[5] Bauer, H., Chapron, G., Nowell, K., Henschel, P., Funston, P., et al. (2015). Lion (Panthera leo) populations are declining rapidly across Africa, except in intensively managed areas. Proceedings of the National Academy of Sciences 112(48): 14894-14899.

[6] Sanderson, E.W., Redford, K.H., Vedder, A., Coppolillo, P.B. and Ward, S.E. (2002). A conceptual model for conservation planning based on landscape species requirements. Landscape and Urban Planning 58: 41-56.

[7] Bauer, H., et al. (2015). Op cit

[8] Ibid

[9] O'Bryan, C.J., Braczkowski, A.R., Beyer, H.L., Carter, N.H., Watson, J.E.M. and McDonald-Madden, E. (2018). The contribution of predators and scavengers to human well-being. Nature Ecology & Evolution 2: 229-236.

PAGES 14-17

[1] Maasai Wilderness Conservation Trust. (2017). http://maasai.com/wp-content/uploads/2017/09/2017-ES-finalcp.pdf (accessed 6/11/2018).

[2] Manthi, F.K., Brown, F.H., Plavcan, M.J. and Werdelin, L. (2018). Gigantic lion, Panthera leo, from the Pleistocene of Natodomeri, eastern Africa. Journal of Paleontology 92(2): 305-312.

[3] Riggio, J.S., Jacobson, A., Dollar, L., Bauer, H., Becker, M., et al. (2013). The size of savannah Africa: A lion's (Panthera leo) view. Biodiversity and Conservation 22(1): 17-35.

[4] Bauer, H., Chapron, G., Nowell, K., Henschel, P., Funston, P., et al. (2015). Lion (Panthera leo) populations are declining rapidly across Africa, except in intensively managed areas. PNAS 112: 14894-14899.

[5] Henschel, P., Coad, L., Burton, C., Chataigner, B., Dunn, A., MacDonald, D., et al. (2014).The Lion in West Africa Is Critically Endangered. PLOS ONE 9(1).

[6] Cushman, S., Elliot, A., Macdonald, N. and Loveridge, B. (2016). A multi-scale assessment of population connectivity in African lions (Panthera leo) in response to landscape change. Landscape Ecology 31(6): 1337-1353.

[7] WWF. (2018). Living Planet Report – 2018: Aiming Higher. WWF, Gland, Switzerland.

[8] Jenkins, C.N., Pimm, S.L. and Joppa, L.N. (2013). Global patterns of terrestrial vertebrate diversity and conservation. Proceedings of the National Academy of Sciences 110.28: E2602-E2610. Source (data layer): BiodiversityMapping.org and IUCN.

[9] Fishpool, L.D.C. and Evans, M.I. (eds.) (2001). Important Bird Areas in Africa and associated islands: Priority sites for conservation. BirdLife Conservation Series No. 11. Pisces Publications and BirdLife International, Newbury and Cambridge, UK.

[10] Jürgens, N., Schmiedel, U. and Hoffman, M.T. (eds.) (2010). Biodiversity in southern Africa. Biota, Göttingen and Windhoek.

[11] Dalerum, F., Somers, M.J., Kunkel, K.E. and Cameron, E.Z. (2008). The potential for large carnivores to act as biodiversity surrogates in southern Africa. Biodiversity Conservation 17: 2939-2949.

[12] https://www.lionrecoveryfund.org (accessed 10/11/2018).

[13] Peterson, A.T., Radocy, T., Hall, E., Kerbis Peterhans, J.C. and Celesia, G.C. (2014). The potential distribution of the Vulnerable African lion Panthera leo in the face of changing global climate. Oryx 48(4): 555-564. DOI:10.1017/S0030605312000919.

[14] Carter, N.H., Bouley, P., Moore, S., Poulos, M., Bouyer, J. and Pimm, S.L. (2018). Climate change, disease range shifts, and the future of the Africa lion. Conservation Biology 32(5). DOI: 10.1111/cobi.13102

[15] Lindsey, P.A., Miller, J.R.B., Petracca, L.S., Coad, L., Dickman, A.J., Fitzgerald, K.H., et al. (2018). More than $1 billion needed annually to secure Africa's protected areas with lions. Proceedings of the National Academy of Sciences 115: 45.

PAGES 18-19

[1] Trouwborst, A., Lewis, M., Burnham, D., Dickman, A., Hinks, A., et al. (2017). International law and lions (Panthera leo): Understanding and improving the contribution of wildlife treaties to the conservation and sustainable use of an iconic carnivore. Nature Conservation 21: 83-128.

[2] IUCN SSC Cat Specialist Group. (2018). Guidelines for the Conservation of Lions in Africa. Version 1.0. Muri/Bern, Switzerland.

[3] Hodgetts, T., Lewis, M., Bauer, H., Burnham, D., Dickman, A., et al. (2018). Improving the role of global conservation treaties in addressing contemporary threats to lions. Biodiversity and Conservation 27(10): 2747-2765.

[4] Ibid

PAGES 20-23

[1] Dr Cristiana Pasca Palmer, UN Assistant Secretary General and Executive Secretary of the Convention on Biological Diversity, remarks at the occasion of the High Level Briefing Session on Biodiversity Finance 6th August 2018, Avani Hotel, Windhoek.

[2] Millennium Ecosystem Assessment. (2005). Ecosystems and human well-being. World Resources Institute, Washington, DC.

[3] Mace, G.M., Norris, K. and Fitter, A.H. (2011). Biodiversity and ecosystem services: A multi-layered relationship. Trends in Ecology and Evolution 27(1): 19-26.

[4] Isbell, F., Craven, D., Connolly, J., Loreau, M., Schmid, B., et al. (2015). Biodiversity increases the resistance of ecosystem productivity to climate extremes. Nature 15374: doi: 10.1038/nature15374.

[5] Gascon, C., Brooks, T.M., Contreras-MacBeath, T., Heard, N., Konstant, W., et al. (2015). The importance and benefits of species. Current Biology 25: R431-R438.

[6] Egoh, B., Reyers, B., Rouget, M., Bode, M. and Richardson, D.M. (2009). Spatial congruence between biodiversity and ecosystem services in South Africa. Biological Conservation 142: 553-562.

[7] Larsen, F.W., Turner, W.R. and Brooks, T.M. (2012). Conserving critical sites for biodiversity provides disproportionate benefits to people. PLoS ONE 7: e36971.

[8] TEEB. (2009). The Economics of Ecosystems and Biodiversity, Summary for Policy Makers. UNEP and EC, Nairobi and Brussels.

[9] Number generated from: http://global-growing.org/en/content/fact-1-majority-sub-saharan-africans-live-rural-areas-europeans-predominantly-cities (accessed 17/4/2019).

[10] IPBES. (2018). The IPBES regional assessment report on biodiversity and ecosystem services for Africa. Archer, E., Dziba, L., Mulongoy, K. J., Maoela, M. A. and Walters, M. (eds.). Secretariat of the Intergovernmental Science-Policy Platform on Biodiversity and Ecosystem Services, Bonn, Germany.

[11] https://www.newvision.co.ug/new_vision/news/1475535/govt-launches-hunt-lions-killers (accessed 31/12/18)

PAGES 24-27

[1] World Tourism Organization. (2014). Towards Measuring the Economic Value of Wildlife Watching Tourism in Africa – Briefing Paper. UNWTO, Madrid.

[2] WTTC. (2018). Travel & Tourism Economic Impact 2018 Zimbabwe, World Travel & Tourism Council (WTTC), London, UK.

[3] Plumptre, A.J. and Roberts, C. (2006). *Attractions of Queen Elizabeth National Park: Perceptions about development of a golf course*. Wildlife Conservation Society, New York.

[4] Van der Merwe, P., Saayman, M., Els, J. and Saayman, A. (2017). The economic significance of lion breeding operations in the South African Wildlife Industry. *International Journal of Biodiversity and Conservation* 9(11): 314-322. DOI: 10.5897/IJBC2017.1103.

[5] Lindsey, P.A., Alexander, R., Mills, M.G.L., Romañach, S. and Woodroffe, R. (2007). Wildlife viewing preferences of visitors to protected areas in South Africa: Implications for the role of ecotourism in conservation. *Journal of Ecotourism* 6(1): 19-33.

[6] Grünewald, C., Schleuning, M. and Böhning-Gaese, K. (2016). Biodiversity, scenery and infrastructure: Factors driving wildlife tourism in an African savannah national park. *Biological Conservation* 201: 60-68.

[7] Willemen, L., Cottam, A.J., Drakou, E.G. and Burgess, N.D. (2015). Using social media to measure the contribution of Red List species to the nature-based tourism potential of African protected areas. *PLoS ONE* 10(6): e0129785. doi:10.1371/journal. pone.0129785.

[8] Naidoo, R., Weaver, L.C., Stuart-Hill, G. and Tagg, J. (2011). Effect of biodiversity on economic benefits from communal lands in Namibia. *Journal of Applied Ecology* 48: 310-316.

[9] Plumptre, A.J. and Roberts, C. (2006). *Op cit.*

[10] https://www.officialdata.org/us/inflation/2006?amount=13500 (accessed 30/12/2018).

[11] Plumptre, A.J. and Roberts, C. (2006). *Op cit.*

[12] Naidoo, R., Fisher, B., Manica, A. and Balmford, A. (2016). Estimating economic losses to tourism in Africa from the illegal killing of elephants. *Nature Communications* 7: 13379. DOI: 10.1038/ncomms13379.

[13] https://www.newtimes.co.rw/section/read/228943 (accessed 10/11/2018).

[14] Cumming, T.L., Shackleton, R.T., Förster, J., Dini, J., Khan, A., et al. (2017). Achieving the national development agenda and the Sustainable Development Goals (SDGs) through investment in ecological infrastructure: A case study of South Africa. *Ecosystem Services* 27 (Part B): 253-260.

[15] NEMA. (2015). *Guidelines and Action Plan for Financing Biodiversity Conservation in Uganda*. National Environment Management Authority, Uganda.

[16] Gereta, E.J., Wolanski, E. and Chiombola, E.A.T. (2003). *Assessment of the Environmental, Social and Economic Impacts on the Serengeti Ecosystem of the Developments in the Mara River Catchment in Kenya*, Tanzania National Parks and Frankfurt Zoological Society, Tanzania.

[17] Emerton, L., Bishop, J. and Thomas, L. (2006). *Sustainable Financing of Protected Areas: A global review of challenges and options*. IUCN, Gland, Switzerland and Cambridge, UK.

[18] Mugizi, F., Ayorekire, J. and Obua, J. (2018). Contribution of tourism to rural community livelihoods in the Murchison Falls Conservation Area, Uganda. *African Journal of Hospitality, Tourism and Leisure* 7(1).

[19] North West CBNRM Forum. (2001). Minutes of the 5th North West District CBNRM Forum, March 29th, 2001, Maun, quoted in: Mbaiwa, J.E. (2004). The socio-cultural impacts of tourism development in the Okavango Delta, Botswana. *Journal of Tourism and Cultural Change* 2(3).

[20] Organisation for Economic Cooperation and Development. (2006). *Why a Healthy Environment is Essential to Reducing Poverty*. OECD, Paris.

[21] Lindsey, P.A., Petracca, L.S., Funston, P.J., Bauer, H., Dickman, A., Everatt, K., et al. (2017). The performance of African protected areas for lions and their prey. *Biological Conservation* 209: 137-149.

[22] Ibid

[23] Backman, K.F. and Munanura, I. (2015). Introduction to the special issues on ecotourism in Africa over the past 30 years. *Journal of Ecotourism* 14: 95-98.

[24] Mbaiwa, J.E. (2003). The socio-economic and environmental impacts of tourism development in the Okavano Delta, north-western Botswana. *Journal of Arid Environments* 54: 447-467.

[25] Lindsey, P.A., Nyirenda, V.R., Barnes, J.I., Becker, M.S., McRobb, R., et al. (2014). Underperformance of African Protected Area Networks and the Case for New Conservation Models: Insights from Zambia. *PLoS ONE* 9(5): e94109. doi:10.1371/journal.pone.0094109.

[26] Watson, F.G.R., Becker, M.S., Millanzi, J. and Nyirenda, M. (2014). Human encroachment into protected area networks in Zambia: Implications for large carnivore conservation. *Regional Environmental Change*. DOI 10.1007/s10113-014-0629-5.

[27] Pfeiffer, M., Burgess, N.D., Swetnam, R.D., Platts, P.J., Willcock, S. and Marchant, R. (2012). Protected areas: Mixed success in conserving East Africa's evergreen forests. *PLoS ONE* 7(6): e39337. doi:10.1371/journal.pone.0039337.

[28] Note there are many different ways of assessing tourism contribution, in this table we have used one source only, World Travel & Tourism Council WTTC. (2018). *Op cit.* for consistency. However different countries report different figures: e.g. see Ministry of Tourism and Wildlife (2018). *National Wildlife Strategy 2030*, Ministry of Tourism & Wildlife, Nairobi, Kenya and https://www.newvision.co.ug/new_vision/news/1475535/govt-launches-hunt-lions-killers (accessed 9/11/2018).

[29] World Travel and Tourism Council. (2018). *Op cit.*

PAGES 28-29

[1] Naidoo, R., Weaver, L.C., Diggle, R.W., Matongo, G., Stuart-Hill, G. and Thoules, C. (2016). Complementary benefits of tourism and hunting to communal conservancies in Namibia. *Conservation Biology* 30: 628-638.

[2] Ministry of Tourism and Wildlife. (2018). *National Wildlife Strategy 2030*. Ministry of Tourism & Wildlife, Nairobi, Kenya.

[3] KWCA. (2017). *Land Rights for Kenya's Community Conservancies Strengthened Community Land Act, 2016 Fact* Sheet 87, https://kwcakenya.com/download/factsheet-community-land-act/?wpdmdl=10443

[4] www.nacssa.co.za (accessed 29/12/2018).

[5] http://www.met.gov.na/services/conservancies/193/ (accessed 29/12/2018).

[6] Lindsey, P.A., Havemann, C.P., Lines, R., Palazy, L., Price, A.E., et al. (2013). Determinants of Persistence and Tolerance of Carnivores on Namibian Ranches: Implications for Conservation on Southern African Private Lands. PLOS ONE 8(1).

[7] Ministry of Tourism and Wildlife. (2018). *Op cit.* Page 55.

[8] Ministry of Tourism and Wildlife (2018). *Op cit.*

[9] For example, the land lease scheme between Nairobi National Park and Kitengela – Athi-Kaputie Plains did not prove to be sustainable. Mbatia, T. (2015). Management of Nairobi National Park, Viabilities, Futures and Strategies of Sustaining an Urban Protected Area, A Critique of the Wildlife Conservation Lease Programme in the Kitengela Wildlife Dispersal Area, University of Nairobi, Department of Geography & Environmental Studies, Kenya. http://centredestudisafricans.org/wp-content/uploads/2015/11/Mbatia-Teresa-Barcelona-Paper-1.pdf (accessed 9/10/2018) AND Matiko, D. (2014). Wildlife Conservation Leases are Considerable Conservation Options outside Protected Areas: The Kitengela – Nairobi National Park Wildlife Conservation Lease Program. Journal of Ecosystem and Ecography 4: 146. doi: 10.4172/2157-7625.1000146

[10] Matiko, D. (2014). Wildlife Conservation Leases are Considerable Conservation Options outside Protected Areas: The Kitengela – Nairobi National Park Wildlife Conservation Lease Program. Journal of Ecosystem and Ecography 4: 146. doi: 10.4172/2157-7625.1000146.

[11] For example, the Maasai in the land lease scheme which creates a corridor between Amboseli National Park and Chyulu Hills in Kenya. AfDB. (2015). Payment for environmental services: A promising tool for natural resources management in Africa. AFDB CIF Knowledge Series, African Development Bank Group, Abidjan, Côte d'Ivoire.

[12] Blackburn, S., Hopcraft, J.G.C., Ogutu, J.O., Matthiopoulos, J. and Frank, L. (2016). Human–wildlife conflict, benefit sharing and the survival of lions in pastoralist community-based conservancies. Journal of Applied Ecology 53: 1195-1205. doi: 10.1111/1365-2664.12632.

[13] https://kwcakenya.com/ (accessed 25/10/2018).

[14] Simba is the Swahili word for lion.

[15] MWCT. (2017). Report downloaded at http://maasai.com/wp-content/uploads/2017/09/2017-ES-finalcp.pdf (accessed 25/10/2018).

[16] www.biglife.org (accessed 30/7/2019).

PAGES 30-33

[1] UICN/PACO. (2009). *La grande chasse en Afrique de l'Ouest: quelle contribution à la conservation?* (Big Game Hunting in West Africa. What is its contribution to conservation? IUCN PACO, Ouagadougou, Burkina Faso.

[2] Brink, H., Smith, R.J., Skinner, K. and Leader-Williams, N. (2016). Sustainability and Long Term-Tenure: Lion Trophy Hunting in Tanzania. *PLoS ONE* 11(9): e0162610. doi:10.1371/journal.pone.0162610

3 Lindsey, P.A., Balme, G.A., Booth, V.R., and Midlane, N. (2012). The Significance of African Lions for the Financial Viability of Trophy Hunting and the Maintenance of Wild Land, *PLoS ONE* 7(1): e29332. doi:10.1371/journal.pone.0029332

4 Funston, P.J., Groom, R.J. and Lindsey, P.A. (2013). Insights into the Management of Large Carnivores for Profitable Wildlife-Based Land Uses in African Savannas. *PLoS ONE* 8(3): e59044. doi:10.1371/journal.pone.0059044.

5 Bouché, P., Crosmary, W., Kafando, P., Doamba, B., Kidjo, F.C., et al. (2016). Embargo on lion hunting trophies from West Africa: An effective measure or a threat to lion conservation? *PLoS ONE* 11(5): e0155763. doi:10.1371/journal.pone.0155763.

6 Creel, S., M'soka, J., Dröge, E., Rosenblatt, E., Becker, M.S., et al. (2016). Assessing the sustainability of African lion trophy hunting, with recommendations for policy. *Ecological Applications* 26 (7): 2347-2357.

7 Funston, P.J., et al. (2013). *Op cit.*

8 Syman, A., Jackson, C.R. and Funston, P.J. (2015). The effect of alternative forms of hunting on the social organization of two small populations of lions. *Oryx* 49(4): 604-610. doi:10.1017/S0030605313001336.

9 UICN/PACO (2009). *Op cit.*

10 Lindsey, P.A., et al. (2012). *Op cit.*

11 Southwick Associates. (2015). *The Economic Contributions of Hunting-Related Tourism in Eastern and Southern Africa*, Safari Club International Foundation, Tucson, USA.

12 Murray, C.K. (2017). *The lion's share? On the economic benefits of trophy hunting.* A report for the Humane Society International, prepared by Economists at Large, Melbourne, Australia.

13 Riggio, J., Jacobson, A., Dollar, L., Bauer, H., Becker, M., et al. (2013). The size of savannah Africa: A lion's (*Panthera leo*) view. *Biodiversity and Conservation* 22(1): 17-35.

14 Begg, C.M., Miller, J.R.B. and Begg, K.S. (2018). Effective implementation of age restrictions increases selectivity of sport hunting of the African lion. *Journal of Applied Ecology* 55: 139-146. doi: 10.1111/1365-2664.12951.

15 Jorge, A.A., Vanak, A.T., Thaker, M., Begg, C. and Slotow, R. (2013). Costs and Benefits of the Presence of Leopards to the Sport-Hunting Industry and Local Communities in Niassa National Reserve, Mozambique. *Conservation Biology* 27(4). https://doi.org/10.1111/cobi.12082.

16 Brink, H., Smith, R.J., Skinner, K. and Leader-Williams, N. (2016). Sustainability and long term-tenure: Lion trophy hunting in Tanzania. *PLoS ONE* 11(9): e0162610. doi:10.1371/journal.pone.0162610.

17 Bouché, P., Crosmary, W., Kafando, P., Doamba, B., Kidjo, F.C., et al. (2016). Embargo on lion hunting trophies from West Africa: An effective measure or a threat to lion conservation? *PLoS ONE* 11(5): e0155763. doi:10.1371/journal.pone.0155763

18 Lindsey, P.A., Balme, G.A., Booth, V.R., and Midlane, N. (2012). The Significance of African Lions for the Financial Viability of Trophy Hunting and the Maintenance of Wild Land, *PLoS ONE* 7(1): e29332. doi:10.1371/journal.pone.0029332

19 Hodgetts, T., Lewis, M., Bauer, H., Burnham, D., Dickman, A., et al. (2018). Improving the role of global conservation treaties in addressing contemporary threats to lions. *Biodiversity and Conservation* 27(10): 2747-2765.

20 Lindsey, P.A., Balme, G.A., Funston, P.J., Henschel, P.H. and Hunter, L.T.B. (2016). Life after Cecil: Channelling global outrage into funding for conservation in Africa. *Conservation Letters* 9(4): 296-301.

21 Begg, C.M., Miller, J.R.B. and Begg, K.S. (2018). Effective implementation of age restrictions increases selectivity of sport hunting of the African lion. *Journal of Applied Ecology* 55: 139-146. DOI: 10.1111/1365-2664.12951.

22 Brink, H., Smith, R.J., Skinner, K. and Leader-Williams, N. (2016). Sustainability and long term-tenure: Lion trophy hunting in Tanzania. *PLoS ONE* 11(9): e0162610. doi:10.1371/journal.pone.0162610

23 Brink, H., Smith, R.J., Skinner, K. and Leader-Williams, N. (2016). Sustainability and long term-tenure: Lion trophy hunting in Tanzania. *PLoS ONE* 11(9): e0162610. doi:10.1371/journal.pone.0162610

24 Bauer, H., Nowell, K., Sillero-Zubiri, C. and Macdonald, D.W. (2018). Lions in the modern arena of CITES. *Conservation Letters* 11(5): e12444, doi: 10.1111/conl.12444.

25 https://africageographic.com/blog/skye-the-lion-hunting-furore-parliament-wants-kruger-np-agreement-with-private-reserves-revised/ (accessed 10/11/2018).

26 Creel, S., M'soka, J., Dröge, E., Rosenblatt, E., Becker, M.S., et al. (2016). Assessing the sustainability of African lion trophy hunting, with recommendations for policy. *Ecological Applications* 26(7): 2347-2357.

27 Bouché, P., Crosmary, W., Kafando, P., Doamba, B., Kidjo, F.C., et al. (2016). Embargo on Lion Hunting Trophies from West Africa: An Effective Measure or a Threat to Lion Conservation? *PLoS ONE* 11(5): e0155763. doi:10.1371/journal.pone.0155763.

28 Bouché, P., Crosmary, W., Kafando, P., Doamba, B., Kidjo, F.C., et al. (2016). Embargo on lion hunting trophies from West Africa: An effective measure or a threat to lion conservation? *PLoS ONE* 11(5): e0155763. doi:10.1371/journal.pone.0155763.

29 Lindsey, P.A., Balme, G.A., Booth, V.R., and Midlane, N. (2012). The Significance of African Lions for the Financial Viability of Trophy Hunting and the Maintenance of Wild Land, *PLoS ONE* 7(1): e29332. doi:10.1371/journal.pone.0029332

PAGES 34-41

1 https://www.theguardian.com/environment/2017/aug/13/tanzanias-ghost-safari-how-western-aid-contributed-to-the-decline-of-a-wildlife-haven (accessed 6/11/2018).

2 Burke, S (1), Mulligan, M. (2) and Gutierrez, C. (2) (2019). Ecosystem services provided by the habitat of the African Lion (*Panthera leo*) using Co$ting Nature, Report for Equilibrium Research. (1) AmbioTEK Community Interest Company, UK, (2) Department of Geography, King's College London, UK.

3 United Nations International Strategy for Disaster Reduction. (2015). *Sendai Framework for Disaster Risk Reduction 2015-2030*. United Nations Office for Disaster Risk Reduction, Geneva, Switzerland.

4 Murti, R. and Buyck, C. (eds.). (2014). *Safe Havens: Protected Areas for Disaster Risk Reduction and Climate Change Adaptation*. IUCN, Gland, Switzerland.

5 Humphreys, E., Peden, D., Twomlow, S., Rockström, J., Oweis, T., et al. (2008). *Improving rainwater productivity: Topic 1 synthesis paper*. CGIAR Challenge Program on Water and Food, Colombo.

6 Palmer, A.R. and Bennett, J. (2013). Degradation of communal rangelands in South Africa: Towards an improved understanding to inform policy. *African Journal of Range and Forage Science* 30(1-2): 57-63.

7 Mumba, M. and Thompson, J.R. (2005). Hydrological and ecological impacts of dams on the Kafue Flats floodplain system, southern Zambia. *Physics and Chemistry of the Earth Parts A/B/C* 30(6-7): 442-447.

8 UNDP. (2004). *Evolution of a Disaster Risk Management System: A Case Study from Mozambique*, UNDP Disaster Reduction Unit, Bureau for Crisis Prevention and Recovery, Geneva, Switzerland.

9 FAO. (2004). *Drought impact mitigation and prevention in the Limpopo River Basin: A situation analysis*, FAO Subregional Office for Southern and East Africa Harare.

10 Smithers, J.C., Schulze, R.E., Pike, A. and Jewitt, G.P.W. (2001). A hydrological perspective of the February 2000 floods: A case study in the Sabie River Catchment. *Water SA* 27(3): 325-332.

11 IUCN (undated). The Sabie River: Protecting biodiversity in an internationally important conservation area, IUCN, Gland, Switzerland.

12 Bradshaw, C.J.A., Sodhi, N.S., Peh, K.S.H. and Brook, B.W. (2007). Global evidence that deforestation amplifies flood risk and severity in the developing world. *Global Change Biology* 13: 2379-2395.

13 https://www.nationalgeographic.com/environment/2019/03/why-mozambique-cyclone-idai-was-so-destructive/ (accessed 29/4/2019).

14 IPBES. (2018). *The IPBES regional assessment report on biodiversity and ecosystem services for Africa*. Archer, E., Dziba, L., Mulongoy, K. J., Maoela, M. A. and Walters M. (eds.). Secretariat of the Intergovernmental Science-Policy Platform on Biodiversity and Ecosystem Services, Bonn, Germany.

15 UNEP, WMO and UNCCD. (2016). *Global Assessment of Sand and Dust Storms*. United Nations Environment Programme, Nairobi.

16 https://www.officialdata.org/us/inflation/2007?amount=10 (accessed 30/12/2018).

17 Yaron, G., Mangani, R., Mlava, J., Kambewa, P., Makungwa, S. et al. (2011). *Economic Analysis of Sustainable Natural Resource Use in Malawi*. UNDP UNEP: New York and Nairobi.

18 Renaud, F.G., Sudmeier-Rieux, K. and Estrella, M. (eds.) (2013). *The Role of Ecosystems in Disaster Risk Reduction*. United Nations University Press, New York.

[19] Al-Dousari, A.M. (2009). Recent studies on dust fallout within preserved and open areas in Kuwait. In: Bhat, N.R., Al-Nasser, A.Y. and Omar, S.A.S. (eds.). *Desertification in Arid Lands: Causes, consequences and mitigation.* Kuwait Institute for Scientific Research, Kuwait: 137-147.

[20] Monty, F., Murti, R. and Furuta, N. (2016). *Helping nature help us: Transforming disaster risk reduction through ecosystem management.* IUCN, Gland, Switzerland.

[21] Dudley, N., MacKinnon, K. and Stolton, S. (2015). The role of protected areas in supplying ten critical ecosystem services in drylands: A review. *Biodiversity.* DOI: 10.1080/14888386.2014.928790

[22] Russell, S., Tyrrell, P. and Western, D. (2018). Seasonal interactions of pastoralists and wildlife in relation to pasture in an African savanna ecosystem. *Journal of Arid Environments* 154: 70-81. https://doi.org/10.1016/j.jaridenv.2018.03.007

[23] Thomas, D.S.G., Knight, M. and Wiggs, G.F.S. (2005). Remobilization of Southern African Desert Dune Systems by Twenty-first Century Global Warming. *Nature* 435(7046): 1218-1221. DOI: 10.1038/nature03717

[24] Hayward, M.W., Adendorff, J., O'Brien, J., Sholto-Douglas, A., Bissett, C., et al. (2007). The reintroduction of large carnivores to the Eastern Cape, South Africa: An assessment. *Oryx* 41(2): 205-214.

[25] Sigwela, A., Cowling, R. and Mills, A. (2014). Contribution of protected areas in mitigation against potential impacts of climate change and livelihoods in the Albany Thicket, South Africa. In: Murti, R. and Buyck, C. (eds.). *Safe havens: Protected Areas for Disaster Risk Reduction and Climate Change Adaptation.* IUCN, Gland, Switzerland.

[26] Burke, S (1), Mulligan, M. (2) and Gutierrez, C. (2) (2019). Ecosystem services provided by the habitat of the African Lion (*Panthera leo*) using Co$ting Nature, Report for Equilibrium Research. (1) AmbioTEK Community Interest Company, UK, (2) Department of Geography, King's College London, UK.

PAGES 42-45

[1] Burke, S (1), Mulligan, M. (2) and Gutierrez, C. (2) (2019). Ecosystem services provided by the habitat of the African Lion (*Panthera leo*) using Co$ting Nature, Report for Equilibrium Research. (1) AmbioTEK Community Interest Company, UK, (2) Department of Geography, King's College London, UK. Carbon sequestration is calculated here from the dry matter productivity (DMP) analysis of Mulligan (2009b) in which SPOT-VGT DMP1 calculated every 10 days at 1 km resolution on the basis of change in NDVI, was averaged over the period 1998-2008, globally. DMP (t biomass/ha/yr) is multiplied by 0.42 (Ho, 1976)[a] to convert to units of tC/ha/yr. Above-ground carbon stock is calculated from Saatchi et al. (2011)[b] for the areas in which data are available and Ruesch and Gibbs (2004)[c] elsewhere. This is combined with soil carbon calculated from the map of Scharlemann et al. (2012)[d] to produce total above- and below-ground carbon stocks. The potential (Cp) and also realised(Cr) carbon service is thus the mean of normalised carbon sequestration (Cs), normalised above-ground carbon stocks (Ca) and normalised below-ground carbon stocks (Cb). [a] Ho, L.C. (1976). Variation in the carbon/dry matter ratio in plant material. *Annals of Botany* 40(165): 163-165, [b] Saatchi, S., Harris, N.L., Brown, S., Lefsky, M., Mitchard, E.T., Salas, W., Zutta, B.R., Buermann, W., Lewis, S.L., Hagen, S., Petrova, S., White, L., Silman, M. and Morel, A. (2011). Benchmark map of forest carbon stocks in tropical regions across three continents. *PNAS* 108 (24): 9899-9904. [c] Ruesch, A. and Gibbs, H.K. (2008). New IPCC Tier-1 Global Biomass Carbon Map for the Year 2000. Available online from the Carbon Dioxide Information Analysis Center [http://cdiac.ess-dive.lbl.gov], Oak Ridge National Laboratory, Oak Ridge, Tennessee. [d] Scharlemann, J.P.W., Hiederer, R. and Kapos, V. (2012). *Global map of terrestrial soil organic carbon stocks.* A 1-km dataset derived from the Harmonized World Soil Database. UNEP-WCMC & EU-JRC, Cambridge, UK.

[2] Scharlemann, J.P.W., Kapos, V., Campbell, A., Lysenko, I., Burgess, N.D., et al. (2010). Securing tropical forest carbon: The contribution of protected areas to REDD. *Oryx* 44(3): 352-357.

[3] Fahey, T.J., Woodbury, P.B., Battles, J.J., Goodale, C.L., Hamburg, S., et al. (2009). Forest carbon storage: Ecology, management and storage. *Frontiers of Ecology and Environment.* doi:10.1890/080169.

[4] Pelletier, J., Paquette, A., Mbindo, K., Zimba, N., Siampale, A., et al. (2018). Carbon sink despite large deforestation in African dry tropical forests (miombo woodlands). *Environment Research Letters* 13: 094017. https://doi.org/10.1088/1748-9326/aadc9a.

[5] Millennium Ecosystem Assessment. (2005). *Global Drylands: A UN Systems-Wide Report.* United Nations, New York.

[6] Grace, J., José, J.S., Meir, P. Miranda, H.S. and Montes, R.A. (2006). Productivity and carbon fluxes of tropical savannas. *Journal of Biogeography* 33: 387-400.

[7] IPBES (2018). *The IPBES regional assessment report on biodiversity and ecosystem services for Africa.* Archer, E., Dziba, L., Mulongoy, K. J., Maoela, M. A. and Walters, M. (eds.). Secretariat of the Intergovernmental Science-Policy Platform on Biodiversity and Ecosystem Services, Bonn, Germany.

[8] Shirima, D.D., Munishi, P.K.T., Lewis, S.L., Burgess, N.D., Marshall, A.R., et al. (2011). Carbon storage, structure and composition of miombo woodlands in Tanzania's Eastern Arc Mountains. *African Journal of Ecology* 49: 332-342.

[9] Munishi, P.K.T., Mringi, S., Shirima, D.D. and Linda, S.K. (2010). The role of the miombo woodlands of the Southern highlands of Tanzania as carbon sinks. *Journal of Ecology and the Natural Environment* 2(12): 261-269.

[10] Ryan, C.M., Hill, T., Woolen, E., Ghee, C., Mitchard, E., et al. (2011). Quantifying small-scale deforestation and forest degradation in African woodlands using radar imagery. *Global Change Biology* 18: 243-257 doi: 10.1111/j.1365-2486.2011.02551.x.

[11] Jew, E.K.K., Dougill, A.J., Sallu, S.M., O'Connell, J. and Benton, T.G. (2016). Miombo woodland under threat: Consequences for tree diversity and carbon storage. *Forest Ecology and Management* 361(1): 144-153.

[12] Ryan, C.M., Williams, M. and Grace, J. (2010). Above- and below-ground carbon stocks in a miombo woodland landscape of Mozambique. *Biotropica* 10. 1111/j.1744-7429.2010.00713.x.

[13] Williams, M., Ryan, C.M., Rees, R.M., Sambane, E., Fernando, J. and Grace, J. (2007). Carbon sequestration and biodiversity of re-growing miombo woodlands in Mozambique. *Forest Ecology and Management* 254(2): 145-155.

[14] Walker, S.R. and Desanker, P.V. (2004). The impact of land use on soil carbon in miombo woodland in Malawi. *Forest Ecology and Management* 203: 345-360.

[15] Kalaba, F.K., Quinn, C.H., Dougill, A.J. and Vinya, R. (2013). Floristic composition, species diversity and carbon storage in agriculture fallows and management implications in Miombo woodlands in Zambia. *Forest Ecology and Management* 304: 99-109.

[16] Burke, S. et al. (2019). *Op cit.*

[17] Lupala, Z.J., Lusambo, L.P. and Ngaga, Y.M. (2014). Management, growth and carbon storage in miombo woodlands in Tanzania. *International Journal of Forestry Research* Article ID 629317.

[18] Prices updated to 2019 value. https://www.officialdata.org/us/inflation/2007?amount=630 (accessed 31/1/2019).

[19] Marunda, C. and Bouda, H-N. (2010). Environmental Services from the Dry Forests and Woodlands of Sub-Saharan Africa, in Chidumayo, E.N. and Gumbo, D.J. (eds.) *The dry forests and woodlands of Africa: Managing for products and services,* Earthscan, London.

[20] Pers comm. [1/11/2018] Erica Meta Smith, Terra Global, www.terraglobalcapital.com

[21] https://theredddesk.org/countries/Malawi

[22] https://www.wildlifeworks.com/kenya (accessed 31/10/2018).

[23] Conservation International. Undated. Case study: The Chyulu Hills REDD+ project. 2 page information sheet. Gabarone.

[24] www.carbontanzania.com/ (accessed 29/4/2019).

PAGES 46-47

[1] African Development Bank Group. (2014). *Payment for Environmental Services. A promising tool for Natural Resources Management in Africa.* African Development Bank Group, Abidjan, Côte d'Ivoire.

[2] USAID. (2018). *Experiences and lessons learned in payments for ecosystem services (PES) in East Africa.* Tetra Tech, USA and Land Trees and Sustainability Africa (LTSA), Nairobi.

[3] van der Gaast, W., Sikkema, R. and Vohrer, M. (2018). The contribution of forest carbon credit projects to addressing the climate change challenge. *Climate Policy* 18(1): 42-48. DOI: 10.1080/14693062.2016.1242056.

[4] USAID. (2018). *Op cit.*

[5] van der Gaast, W., et al. (2018). *Op cit.*

[6] http://www.greenclimate.fund (accessed 29/4/2019).

[7] World Bank and Ecofys (2018). *State and Trends of Carbon Pricing 2018,* World Bank, Washington, DC. Doi: 10.1596/978-1-4648-1292-7.

[8] van der Gaast, W., et al. (2018). *Op cit.*

[9] Sena, K. (2015). Carbon credit schemes and indigenous peoples in Kenya: A commentary. *Arizona Journal of International & Comparative Law* 32(1).

[10] World Bank and Ecofys (2018). *State and Trends of Carbon Pricing 2018*, World Bank, Washington, DC. Doi: 10.1596/978-1-4648-1292-7.

[11] Mabeta, J., Mweemba, B. and Mwitwa, J. (2018). *Key drivers of biodiversity loss in Zambia*, Biodiversity Finance Initiative (BIOFIN) (2018), Zambia Policy Brief # 3. February 2018

[12] http://blog.biocarbonpartners.com/ (accessed 12/2/2019).

[13] Ibid

PAGES 48-49

[1] WWF Kenya. (2017). Kenya's Water Resource User Associations: Devolving responsibility for water management in the Mara river basin, WWF Kenya, Nairobi.

[2] Beilfuss, R. (2012). A Risky Climate for Southern African Hydro: Assessing Hydrological Risks and Consequences for Zambezi River Basin Dams. International Rivers, Berkeley, USA.

[3] Gregory, P.J., Ingram, J.S.I. and Brklacich, M. (2005). Climate change and food security. Philosophical Transactions of the Royal Society 360: 2139-2148.

[4] Mayers, J., Batchelor, C., Bond, I., Hope, R., Morrison, E. and Wheeler, B. (2009). Water ecosystem services and poverty under climate change: Key issues and research priorities. IIED, London.

[5] Patz, J.A., Campbell-Lendrum, D., Holloway, T. and Foley, J.A. (2005). Impact of regional climate change on human health. Nature 438: 310-317.

[6] https://gain.nd.edu/our-work/country-index/methodology/ (accessed 13/12/2018).

[7] https://gain.nd.edu/our-work/country-index/rankings/ (accessed 13/12/2018).

[8] Oliver, T.H., Isaac, N.J.B., August, T.A., Woodcock, B.A., Roy, D.B, et al. (2015). Declining resilience of ecosystem functions under biodiversity loss. Nature Communications. DOI: 10.1038/ncomms10122.

[9] Thompson, I., Mackey, B., McNulty, S. and Mosseler, A. (2009). Forest Resilience, Biodiversity, and Climate Change: A synthesis of the biodiversity/resilience/stability relationship in forest ecosystems, CBD Technical Series no. 43, Secretariat of the Convention on Biological Diversity, Montreal.

[10] Kapos V., Ravilious, C., Campbell, A., Dickson, B., Gibbs, H.K., et al. (2008). Carbon and biodiversity: A demonstration atlas, UNEP-WCMC, Cambridge, UK.

[11] Fanaian, S., Graas, S., Jiang, Y. and van der Zaag, P. (2015). An ecological economic assessment of flow regimes in a hydropower dominated river basin: The case of the lower Zambezi River, Mozambique. Science of the Total Environment 505: 464-473.

[12] Andrade Pérez, A., Herera Fernández, B. and Cazzolla Gatti, R. (eds.) (2010). Building Resilience to Climate Change: Ecosystem-based adaptation and lessons from the field. IUCN Commission on Ecosystem Management, Ecosystem Management Series number 9, IUCN, Gland, Switzerland.

[13] Epple, C. and Dunning, E. (2014). Ecosystem resilience to climate change: What is it and how can it be addressed in the context of climate change adaptation? Technical report for the Mountain EbA Project. UNEP World Conservation Monitoring Centre, Cambridge, UK.

[14] Hoogendoorn, G. and Fitchett, J.M. (2018). Tourism and climate change: A review of threats and adaptation strategies for Africa. Current *Issues in Tourism* 21(7). DOI: 10.1080/13683500.2016.1188893

PAGES 50-51

[1] UNEP. (2010). *Africa Water Atlas.* Division of Early Warning and Assessment (DEWA). United Nations Environment Programme (UNEP). Nairobi, Kenya.

[2] IPBES. (2018). *The IPBES regional assessment report on biodiversity and ecosystem services for Africa.* Archer, E., Dziba, L., Mulongoy, K. J., Maoela, M. A. and Walters, M. (eds.). Secretariat of the Intergovernmental Science-Policy Platform on Biodiversity and Ecosystem Services, Bonn, Germany.

[3] Naik, P.K. (2017). Water crisis in Africa: Myth or reality? *International Journal of Water Resources Development* 33(2): 326-329. DOI: 10.1080/07900627.2016.1188266.

[4] Overseas Development Institute. (2017). Making water infrastructure investment decisions in a changing climate. A political economy study of river basin development in Kenya. Overseas Development Institute, London, UK.

[5] Falkenmark, M. (2018). Shift in Water Thinking Crucial for Sub-Saharan Africa's Future. In: Biswas, A.K., Tortajada, C. and Rohner, P. (eds.) *Assessing Global Water Megatrends*. Springer, Singapore. DOI: https://doi.org/10.1007/978-981-10-6695-5

[6] Adekola, O., Morardet, S., De Groot, R. and Grelot, F. (2008). The economic and livelihood value of provisioning services in the Ga-Mampa wetland, South Africa. In: IWRA World Water Congress, Montpellier, France.

[7] Burke, S., Mulligan, M. and Gutierrez, C. (2018). *Ecosystem services provided by the habitat of the African Lion* (Panthera leo), Co$ting Nature. Report for Equilibrium Research.

[8] Celesia, G., Townsend Peterson, A., Kerbis Peterhans, J. and Gnoske, T. (2010). Climate and landscape correlates of African lion (*Panthera leo*) demography. *African Journal of Ecology* 48(1): 58-71.

[9] Mills, M.G.L., Biggs, H.C. and Whyte, I.J. (1995). The relationship between rainfall, lion predation and population trends in African carnivores. *Wildlife Research* 22: 75-87.

[10] https://www.lilongwewildlife.org/national-parks-wilderness-reserves/ (accessed 15/10/2018).

[11] NEPAD. Undated. Country Water Resource Profile, New Partnership for Africa's Development Water Centres of Excellence.

[12] Mésochina, P., Sefu, L., Sichali, E., Chardonnet, P., Ngalande, J. and Lipita, W. (2010). *Conservation status of the lion (Panthera leo) in Malawi*, SCI Foundation and DNPW, Paris, France.

[13] Riggio, J., Jacobson, A., Dollar, L., Bauer, H., Becker, M., et al. (2012). The size of savannah Africa: A lion's (*Panthera leo*) view. *Biodiversity Conservation* 22(1): 17-35.

[14] https://www.africanparks.org/press-release/lions-return (accessed 15/10/2018).

[15] http://leofoundation.org/en/hope-for-waza-nationa-park-in-cameroon/.

[16] IUCN. (2003). Waza Logone Floodplain, Cameroon: Economic benefits of wetland restoration. *Case Studies in Wetland Valuation* #4: IUCN, Gland.

[17] Westra, T. and De Wulf, R.R. (2009). Modelling yearly flooding extent of the WazaLogone floodplain in northern Cameroon based on MODIS and rainfall data. *International Journal of Remote Sensing* 30(21): 5527-5548. DOI: 10.1080/01431160802672872.

[18] Kiringe, J.W., Mwaura, F. and Warinwa, F. (2016). Characterization of Chyulu Hills Watershed Ecosystem Services in South-Eastern Kenya. *Environment and Natural Resources Research* 6(3): 65-76.

[19] Riggio, J., Jacobson, A., Dollar, L., Bauer, H., Becker, M., et al. (2013). The size of savannah Africa: A lion's (*Panthera leo*) view. *Biodiversity Conservation* 22: 17-35. https://doi.org/10.1007/s10531-012-0381-4

[20] United Nations Development Programme. (2013). *Maasai Wilderness Conservation Trust, Kenya.* Equator Initiative Case Study Series. New York, NY.

[21] Muriuki, G., Seabrook, L., McAlpine, C., Jacobson, C., Price, B. and Baxter, G. (2011). Land cover change under unplanned settlements: A study of the Chyulu Hills squatters, Kenya. *Landscape and Urban Planning* 99: 154-165.

PAGES 52-53

[1] https://support.worldwildlife.org/site/Advocacy?cmd=display&page=UserAction&id=979 (accessed 4/11/2018).

[2] https://www.worldwildlife.org/stories/chief-stands-against-proposed-dam-on-luangwa-river (accessed 4/11/2018).

[3] Beilfuss, R. (2012). *A Risky Climate for Southern African Hydro: Assessing Hydrological Risks and Consequences for Zambezi River Basin Dams.* International Rivers, Berkeley, USA.

[4] Mweetwa, T., Christianson, D., Becker, M., Creel, S., Rosenblatt, E., et al. (2018). Quantifying lion (*Panthera leo*) demographic response following a three-year moratorium on trophy hunting. *PLoS ONE* 13(5): e0197030. https://doi.org/10.1371/journal.pone.0197030.

[5] Beilfuss, R. (2012). *Op cit.*

[6] Mweetwa, T., et al. (2018). *Op cit.*

[7] Beilfuss, R. (2012). *Op cit.*

[8] https://support.worldwildlife.org/site/Advocacy?cmd=display&page=UserAction&id=979 (accessed 4/11/2018).

[9] https://www.officialdata.org/us/inflation/2001?amount=10 (accessed 30/12/2018).

[10] Seyam, I.M., Hoekstra, A.Y., Ngabirano, G.S. and Saveninje, H.H.G. (2001). *The Value of Freshwater Wetlands in the Zambezi Basin*. Value of Water Research Report Series No. 7. International Institute for Infrastructural Hydraulic and Environmental Engineering (IHE). Delft, The Netherlands.

PAGES 54-55

[1] Hodgetts, T., Lewis, M., Bauer, H., Burnham, D., Dickman, A., et al. (2018). Improving the role of global conservation treaties in addressing contemporary threats to lions. *Biodiversity and Conservation* 27(10): 2747-2765.

[2] Davies, J. and Hatfield, R. (2007). The economics of mobile pastoralism: A global summary. *Nomadic Peoples* 11(1): 91-116.

[3] IPBES. (2018). *The IPBES regional assessment report on biodiversity and ecosystem services for Africa.* Archer, E., Dziba, L., Mulongoy, K. J., Maoela, M. A. and Walters, M. (eds.). Secretariat of the Intergovernmental Science-Policy Platform on Biodiversity and Ecosystem Services, Bonn, Germany.

[4] Grandval, F. (2012). Pastoralism in Sub-Saharan Africa: Know its advantages, understand its challenges, act for its sustainability. *Food Sovereignty Briefs,* Inter-Réseaux Développement Rural and SOS Faim Belgium.

[5] Lindsey, P.A., Havemann, C.P., Lines, R., Palazy, L., Price, A.E., et al. (2013). Determinants of persistence and tolerance of carnivores on Namibian ranches: Implications for conservation on southern African private lands. *PLoS ONE* 8(1): e52458. doi:10.1371/journal.pone.0052458.

[6] Hemson, G., Maclennan, S., Mills, G., Johnson, P. and Macdonald, D. (2009). Community, lions, livestock and money: A spatial and social analysis of attitudes to wildlife and the conservation value of tourism in a human–carnivore conflict in Botswana. *Biological Conservation* 142: 2718-2725.

[7] Tumenta, P., De Iongh, H., Funston, P. and Udo de Haes, H. (2013). Livestock depredation and mitigation methods practised by resident and nomadic pastoralists around Waza National Park, Cameroon. *Oryx* 47(2): 237-242. doi:10.1017/S0030605311001621.

[8] Basupi, L.V., Quinn, C.H. and Dougill, A.J. (2017). Pastoralism and Land Tenure Transformation in Sub-Saharan Africa: Conflicting Policies and Priorities in Ngamiland, Botswana. *Land* 6 (89). doi:10.3390/land6040089

[9] Blackburn, S., Hopcraft, J.G.C., Ogutu, J.O., Matthiopoulos, J. and Frank, L. (2016). Human–wildlife conflict, benefit sharing and the survival of lions in pastoralist community-based conservancies. *Journal of Applied Ecology* 53: 1195-1205. doi: 10.1111/1365-2664.12632.

[10] Maclennan, S.D., Groom, R.J., Macdonald, D.W. and Frank, L.G. (2009). Evaluation of a compensation scheme to bring about pastoralist tolerance of lions. *Biological Conservation* 142: 2419-2427.

[11] Mkonyi, F.J., Estes, A.B., Msuha, M.J., Lichtenfeld, L.L. and Durant, S.M. (2017). Socio-economic correlates and management implications of livestock depredation by large carnivores in the Tarangire ecosystem, northern Tanzania, *International Journal of Biodiversity Science, Ecosystem Services & Management* 13(1): 248-263. DOI: 10.1080/21513732.2017.1339734

[12] Dickman, A., Hazzah, L., Carbone, C. and Durant, S.M. (2014). Carnivores, culture and "contagious conflict": Multiple factors influence perceived problems with carnivores in Tanzania's Ruaha landscape. *Biological Conservation* 178: 19-27.

[13] https://www.independent.co.uk/news/world/africa/uganda-lions-killed-poisoning-queen-elizabeth-national-park-wildlife-protection-investigation-a8302606.html (accessed 9/10/2018).

[14] Lichtenfeld, L.L., Trout, C. and Kisimir, E.L. (2015). Evidence-based conservation: predatorproof bomas protect livestock and lions. *Biodiversity Conservation* 24: 483-491. DOI 10.1007/s10531-014-0828-x

[15] Mkonyi, F.J., et al. (2017). *Op cit.*

[16] Tyrrell, P., Russell, S. and Western, D. (2017). Seasonal movements of wildlife and livestock in a heterogenous pastoral landscape: Implications for coexistence and community based conservation. *Global Ecology and Conservation* 12: 59e72.

[17] Russell, S., Tyrrell, P. and Western, D. (2018). Seasonal interactions of pastoralists and wildlife in relation to pasture in an African savanna ecosystem. *Journal of Arid Environments* 154: 70-81. https://doi.org/10.1016/j.jaridenv.2018.03.007

[18] Anyango-van Zwieten, N., Van Der Duim, R. and Visseren-Hamakers, I. (2015). Compensating for livestock killed by lions: Payment for environmental services as a policy arrangement. *Environmental Conservation* 42(4): 363-372. doi:10.1017/S0376892915000090.

[19] Western, G., Macdonald, D.W., Loveridge, A.J. and Dickman, A.J. (2019). Creating Landscapes of Coexistence: Do Conservation Interventions Promote Tolerance of Lions in Human-dominated Landscapes? *Conservation and Society* 17(2): 204-217.

[20] Blackburn, S., et al. (2016). *Op cit.*

[21] Ibid

[22] https://blog.nationalgeographic.org/2016/05/22/bucking-the-trend-lion-recoveries-on-community-lands/ (accessed 10/11/2018).

[23] Schuette, P., Creel, S. and Christianson, D. (2013). Coexistence of African lions, livestock, and people in a landscape with variable human land use and seasonal movements. *Biological Conservation* 157: 148-154.

[24] Creel, S., Christianson, D. and Schuette, P. (2013). Glucocorticoid stress responses of lions in relationship to group composition, human land use, and proximity to people, *Conservation Physiology* 1(1): https://doi.org/10.1093/conphys/cot021.

[25] Tyrrell, P., et al. (2017). *Op cit.*

[26] Russell, S., et al. (2018). *Op cit.*

[27] http://soralo.org/rebuilding-pride/ (accessed 15/10/2018).

[28] http://global-growing.org/en/content/linking-livestock-markets-wildlife-conservation (accessed 15/10/2018).

[29] https://www.conservation-capital.com/cows-for-conservation (accessed 9/10/2018).

[30] For example, the Maasai in the land lease scheme which creates a corridor between Amboseli National Park and Chyulu Hills in Kenya. AfDB. (2015). *Payment for environmental services: A promising tool for natural resources management in Africa.* AFDB CIF Knowledge Series, African Development Bank Group, Abidjan, Côte d'Ivoire.

[31] http://www.tawilodge.com/ (accessed 30/12/2018).

[32] AfDB. (2015). *Op cit.*

PAGES 56-59

[1] https://reliefweb.int/report/world/new-programme-boost-soil-productivity-and-reduce-soil-degradation-africa (accessed 1/1/2019).

[2] Bond, I., Chambwera, M., Jones, B., Chundama, M. and Nhantumbo, I. (2010). REDD+ in dryland forests: Issues and prospects for pro-poor REDD in the Miombo woodlands of southern Africa. *Natural Resource Issues* No. 21. IIED, London.

[3] Von Maltitz, G. and Setzkorn, K. (2012). Potential impacts of biofuels on deforestation in Southern Africa. *Journal of Sustainable Forestry* 31: 80-97.

[4] Cheremshynskyi, M. and Byamugisha, F.F.K. (2014). Developing land information systems in Sub-Saharan Africa: Experiences and lessons from Uganda and Ghana. In: Byamugisha, F.F.K (ed.) *Agricultural Land Redistribution and Land Administration in Sub-Saharan Africa: Case Studies of Recent Reforms*: 103-116. World Bank, Washington, DC.

[5] Herrero, M., Havlik, P., McIntire, J., Palazzo, A. and Valin, H. (2014). *African Livestock Futures: Realizing the Potential of Livestock for Food Security, Poverty Reduction and the Environment in Sub-Saharan Africa.* Office of the Special Representative of the UN Secretary General for Food Security and Nutrition and the United Nations System Influenza Coordination (UNSIC), Geneva, Switzerland.

[6] Dudley, N. and Alexander, S. (2017). *Global Land Outlook.* UN Convention to Combat Desertification, Bonn.

[7] Gomes, N. (2006). Access to water, pastoral resource management and pastoralists' livelihoods: Lessons learned from water development in selected areas of Eastern Africa (Kenya, Ethiopia, Somalia). LSP Working Paper 26. FAO, Rome.

[8] Biggs, R., Simons, H., Bakkenes, M., Scholes, R.J., Eickhout, B., et al. (2008). Scenarios of biodiversity loss in southern Africa in the 21st century. *Global Environmental Change* 18: 296-309.

[9] Venter, Z.S., Hawkins, H.J. and Cramer, M.D. (2017). Implications of historical interactions between herbivory and fire for rangeland management in African savannas. *Ecosphere* 8(10): e01900. 10.1002/ecs2.1946

[10] Falkenmark, M. (2018). Shift in Water Thinking Crucial for Sub-Saharan Africa's Future. In: Biswas, A.K., Tortajada, C., Rohner, P. (eds.) *Assessing Global Water Megatrends.* Springer, Singapore. doi.org/10.1007/978-981-10-6695-5.

[11] Van Zyl, H. (2015). *The economic value and potential of protected areas in Ethiopia.* Report for the Ethiopian Wildlife Conservation Authority under the Sustainable Development of the Protected Areas System of Ethiopia Programme (Independent Economic Researchers, Cape Town, South Africa).

[12] Bauer, H. and Rskay, G. (2015). *Reconnaissance visit to Alatash – Dinder Lion Conservation Unit, Ethiopia –Sudan border.* https://docplayer.net/28610832-Reconnaissance-visit-to-alatash-dinder-lion-conservation-unit-ethiopia-sudan-border-hans-bauer-and-gebeyehu-rskay.html (accessed 15/10/2018).

[13] Bauer, H. (2016). New lion group found in Ethiopia. *New Scientist* 229(3059): 6.

[14] https://justdiggit.org/projects/ (accessed 17/4/2019).

[15] Davies, J. and Hatfield, R. (2008). The economics of mobile pastoralism: A global summary. *Nomadic Peoples* 11(1): 91-116.

[16] Hatfield, R. and Davies, J. (2006). *Global Review of the Economics of Pastoralism*. World Initiative on Sustainable Pastoralism, GEF, UNDP and IUCN, Nairobi.

[17] FAO and Intergovernmental Technical Panel on Soils. (2015). *Status of the World's Soil Resources,* FAO, Rome, Italy.

[18] Russell, S., Tyrrell, P. and Western, D. (2018). Seasonal interactions of pastoralists and wildlife in relation to pasture in an African savanna ecosystem. *Journal of Arid Environments* 154: 70-81. https://doi.org/10.1016/j.jaridenv.2018.03.007

[19] Ibid

[20] Ripple, W.J. and Beschta, R.L. (2012). Large predators limit herbivore densities in northern forest ecosystems. *European Journal of Wildlife Research* 58: 733-742.

[21] Venter, Z.S., et al. (2017). *Op cit.*

[22] Russell, S., et al. (2018). *Op cit.*

[23] Tyrrell, P., Russell, S. and Western, D. (2017). Seasonal movements of wildlife and livestock in a heterogenous pastoral landscape: Implications for coexistence and community based conservation. *Global Ecology and Conservation* 12: 59e72.

[24] Dudley, N. and Alexander, S. (2017). *Op cit.*

[25] Adams, W.M. and Anderson, D.M. (1988). Irrigation before development: Indigenous and induced change in agricultural water management in East Africa. *African Affairs* 87 (349): 519-535.

[26] Riggio, J.S., Jacobson, A., Dollar, L., Bauer, H., Becker, M., Dickman, A., et al. (2013). The size of savannah Africa: A lion's (*Panthera leo*) view. *Biodiversity and Conservation* 22(1): 17-35.

[27] Binot, A., Hanon, L., Joiris, D.V. and Dulieu, D. (2009). The challenge of participatory natural resource management with mobile herders at the scale of a Sub-Saharan African protected area. *Biodiversity and Conservation* 18: 2645-2662.

[28] http://www.acra.it/index.php?option=com_content&view=article&id=532&Itemid=794&lang=en (accessed 1/1/2019).

[29] NEPAD. (2013). *Agriculture in Africa: Transformation and outlook.* NEPAD (New Partnership for African Development), Johannesburg, South Africa.

[30] Leff, J. (2009). Pastoralists at war: Violence and security in the Kenya-Sudan-Uganda border region. *International Journal of Conflict and Violence* 3: 188-203.

[31] Mkonyi, F.J., Estes, A.B., Msuha, M.J., Lichtenfeld, L.L. and Durant, S.M. (2017): Local Attitudes and Perceptions toward Large Carnivores in a Human-Dominated Landscape of Northern Tanzania, *Human Dimensions of Wildlife*. DOI: 10.1080/10871209.2017.1323356

[32] Ondoua Ondoua, G., Beodo Moundjim, E., Mambo Marindo, J.C., Jiagho, R., Usongo, L. and Williamson, L. (2017). *An assessment of poaching and wildlife trafficking in the Garamba-Bili-Chinko transboundary landscape.* TRAFFIC.

PAGES 60-61

[1] https://africa.fsc.org/en-cd/actualits/press-releases/id/297 (accessed 31/10/2018).

[2] Riggio, J., Jacobson, A., Dollar, L., Bauer, H., Becker, M., et al. (2013). The size of savannah Africa: A lion's (*Panthera leo*) view. *Biodiversity and Conservation* 22(1): 17-35.

[3] IPBES. (2018). *The IPBES regional assessment report on biodiversity and ecosystem services for Africa.* Archer, E., Dziba, L., Mulongoy, K.J., Maoela, M.A. and Walters, M. (eds.). Secretariat of the Intergovernmental Science-Policy Platform on Biodiversity and Ecosystem Services, Bonn, Germany.

[4] Shackleton, C.M., Shackleton, S.E., Buiten, E. and Bird, N. (2007). The importance of dry woodlands and forests in rural livelihoods and poverty alleviation in South Africa. *Forest Policy and Economics* 9: 588-577.

[5] Davenport, N.A., Shackleton, C.M. and Gambiza, J. (2012). The direct use value of municipal commonage goods and services to urban households in the Eastern Cape, South Africa. *Land Use Policy* 29: 548-557.

[6] https://www.reuters.com/article/us-mozambique-forest-logging/mozambique-reforms-timber-sector-to-counter-illegal-logging-idUSKBN1KG1F8 (accessed 15/1/2018).

[7] SGS. (2005). *Forest Management Certification Report: Public Summary. LevasFlor, Lda,* SGS South Africa, Southdale, South Africa.

[8] http://www.levasflor.com/ (accessed 31/10/2018).

[9] https://africa.fsc.org/en-cd/actualits/press-releases/id/297 (accessed 31/10/2018).

[10] http://www.levasflor.com/ (accessed 31/10/2018).

[11] SGS. (2005). *Op cit.*

PAGES 62-63

[1] FAO. (2019). *The State of the World's Biodiversity for Food and Agriculture.* Commission on Genetic Resources for Food and Agriculture, FAO, Rome.

[2] FAO. (2018). *Biodiversity for Sustainable Agriculture: FAO's work on biodiversity for food and agriculture.* Food and Agricultural Organization, Rome.

[3] Ollerton, J., Winfree, R. and Tarrant, S. (2011). How many flowering plants are pollinated by animals? *Oikos* 120(3): 321-326.

[4] Klein, A.M., Vaissiere, B.E., Cane, J.H., Steffan-Dewenter, I., Cunningham, S.A., et al. (2007). Importance of pollinators in changing landscapes for world crops. *Proceedings of the Royal Society B: Biological Sciences* 274 (1608): 303-313.

[5] Klatt, B., Olzschuh, A., Westphal, C., Clough, Y. Smiut, I., et al. (2014). Bee pollination improves crop quality, shelf life and commercial value. *Proceedings of the Royal Society B* 281: DOI: 10.1098/rspb.2013.2440.

[6] Garibaldi, L.A., Steffan-Dewenter, I., Winfree, R., Aizen, M.A., Bommarco, R., et al. (2013). Wild pollinators enhance fruit set of crops regardless of honey bee abundance. *Science* 340(6127): 1608-1611.

[7] Kremen, C., Williams, N.M. and Thorp, R.W. (2002). Crop pollination from native bees at risk from agricultural intensification. *Proceedings of the National Academy of Sciences* 99(26): 16812-16816.

[8] Goulson, D., Nicholls, E., Botias, C. and Rotheray, E.L. (2015). Bee declines driven by combined stress from parasites, pesticides and lack of flowers. *Science* 347(6229): DOI: 10.1126/science.1255957.

[9] IPBES. (2016). *The assessment report on pollinators, pollination and food production of the 2821 Intergovernmental Science-policy Platform on Biodiversity and Ecosystem Services.* S.G. Potts, V.L. Imperatriz-Fonseca and H.T. Ngo (eds.) Bonn, Germany, Secretariat of the Intergovernmental Science-2823 Policy Platform on Biodiversity and Ecosystem Services.

[10] Forrest, J.R.K., Thorp, R.W., Kremen, C. and Williams, N. (2015). Contrasting patterns in species and functional-trait diversity of bees in an agricultural landscape. *Journal of Applied Ecology.* DOI: 10.1111/1365-2664.12433

[11] Mushambanyi, B. and Munyuli, T. (2014). Social and ecological drivers of the economic value of pollination services delivered to coffee in central Uganda. *Journal of Ecosystems.* http://dx.doi.org/10.1155/2014/298141

[12] Yaron, G., Mangani, R., Mlava, J., Kambewa, P., Makungwa, S., et al. (2011). *Economic Analysis of Sustainable Natural Resource Use in Malawi.* UNDP UNEP.

[13] Sacande, M. and Parfondry, M. (2018). *Non-timber forest products: From restoration to income generation.* Rome, FAO. 40 pp.

[14] Yaron, G., et al. (2011). *Op cit.*

[15] Seyam, I.M., Hoekstra, A.Y., Ngabirano, G.S. and Saveninje, H.H.G. (2001). *The Value of Freshwater Wetlands in the Zambezi Basin.* Value of Water Research Report Series No. 7. International Institute for Infrastructural Hydraulic and Environmental Engineering (IHE). Delft, The Netherlands.

[16] IPBES. (2018). *The IPBES regional assessment report on biodiversity and ecosystem services for Africa.* Archer, E., Dziba, L., Mulongoy, K.J., Maoela, M.A. and Walters, M. (eds.). Secretariat of the Intergovernmental Science-Policy Platform on Biodiversity and Ecosystem Services, Bonn, Germany.

[17] Ripple, W.J., Estes, J.A., Beschta, R.L., Wilmers, C.C., Ritchie, E.G., et al. (2014). Status and ecological effects of the world's largest carnivores. *Science* 343: DOI: 10.1126/science.1241484.

[18] Brashares, J.S., Prugh, L.R., Stoner, C.J. and Epps, C.W. (2010). Ecological and conservation implications of mesopredator release. In: Terbrough, J. and Estes, J.A. (eds.) *Trophic Cascades: Predators, prey and the changing dynamics of nature.* Island Press, Washington DC: 221-240.

[19] Taylor, R.A., Ryan, S.J., Brashares, J.S. and Johnson, L.R. (2016). Hunting, food subsidies, and mesopredator release: The dynamics of crop-raiding baboons in a managed landscape. *Ecology* 97: 951-960.

[20] Maxted, N., Ford-Lloyd, B.V., Jury, S.L., Kell S.P. and Scholten M.A. (2006). Towards a definition of a crop wild relative. *Biodiversity and Conservation* 14: 1-13.

[21] Meilleur, B.A. and Hodgkin, T. (2004). *In situ* conservation of crop wild relatives: Status and trends. *Biodiversity and Conservation* 13: 663-684.

[22] Prescott-Allen, R. and Prescott-Allen, C. (1984). Park your genes: Protected areas as *in situ* gene banks for the maintenance of wild genetic resources. In: McNeely, J.A. and Miller, K.R. (eds.) *National Parks, Conservation, and Development: The Role of Protected Areas in Sustaining Society,* Smithsonian Institution Press, Washington DC: 634-638.

[23] Davis, A.P., Chadburn, H., Moat, J., O'Sullivan, R., Hargreaves, S. and Lughadha, E.N. (2019). High extinction risk for wild coffee species and implications for coffee sector sustainability. *Science Advances* 5: eaav3473.

[24] Groombridge, B. (1992). *Global Biodiversity: Status of the Earth's Living Resources*, WCMC with Chapman and Hall, London.

[25] Burgess, N., D'Amico Hales, J., Underwood, E., Dinerstein, E., Olson, D., et al. (2004). *Terrestrial ecoregions of Africa and Madagascar: A continental assessment,* Island Press, Washington DC: 262.

[26] Van Zyl, H. (2015). *The economic value and potential of protected areas in Ethiopia.* Report for the Ethiopian Wildlife Conservation Authority under the Sustainable Development of the Protected Areas System of Ethiopia Programme (Independent Economic Researchers, Cape Town, South Africa).

[27] http://wetlandsandforests.hud.ac.uk/forests/wcc/project.html (accessed 30/12/2018).

[28] Ingram, G. (1990). Multi-gene pool surveys in areas with rapid genetic erosion: An example from the Aïr Mountains, northern Niger. *Conservation Biology* 4: 78-90.

[29] Davis, S.D., Heywood, V.H. and Hamilton, A.C. (1994). *Centres of plant diversity. A guide and strategy for their conservation*, 3 volumes, IUCN, Cambridge, UK and WWF, Gland, Switzerland.

[30] Oryem-Origa, H., Kasenene, J.M. and Magambo, M.J.S. (2004). Some aspects of wild robusta coffee seedling growth in Kibale National Park, Uganda. *African Journal of Ecology* 42(s1): 34-39.

PAGES 64-65

[1] http://www.krugerpark.co.za/krugerpark-times-6-2-mopani-worm-harvest-25325.html (accessed 7/11/2018).

[2] https://www.worldwildlife.org/ecoregions/at0725 (accessed 6/11/2018).

[3] Gandiwa, E. (2011). Importance of savanna woodlands in rural livelihoods and wildlife conservation in southeastern Zimbabwe. In: Bojang, F. (ed.). The forest sector in the green economy in Africa, *Nature & Faune*, 26(1).

[4] Makhado, R., Potgieter, M., Timberlake, J. and Gumbo, D. (2014). A review of the significance of mopane products to rural people's livelihoods in southern Africa. *Transactions of the Royal Society of South Africa,* 69(2): 117-122. DOI: 10.1080/0035919X.2014.922512.

[5] Gondo, T., Frost, P., Kozanayi, W., Stack, J. and Mushongahande, M. (2010). Linking knowledge and practice: Assessing options for sustainable use of mopane worms (*Imbrasia belina*) in southern Zimbabwe. *Journal of Sustainable Development in Africa* 12(1): 281-305.

[6] Makhado, R., et al. (2014). *Op cit.*

[7] Ibid

[8] Ibid

[9] Benisiu, T. (2013). Sustainable harvesting and trading of mopane worms (*Imbrasiabelina*) in Northern Namibia: An experience from the Uukwaluudhi area *International Journal of Environmental Studies* 70(4): 494-502. DOI: 10.1080/00207233.2013.829324.

[10] Makhado, R., et al. (2014). *Op cit.*

[11] Benisiu, T. (2013). Sustainable harvesting and trading of mopane worms (*Imbrasia belina*) in Northern Namibia: An experience from the Uukwaluudhi area. *International Journal of Environmental Studies* 70(4): 494-502. DOI: 10.1080/00207233.2013.829324.

[12] Maviya, J. and Gumbo, D. (2005). Incorporating traditional natural resource management techniques in conventional natural resources management strategies: A case of Mopane worms (*Amacimbi*) management and harvesting in the Bulilimamangwe District, Zimbabwe. *Journal of Sustainable Development in Africa* 7(2).

[13] http://www.krugerpark.co.za/krugerpark-times-6-2-mopani-worm-harvest-25325.html (accessed 7/11/2018).

[14] https://www.news24.com/Green/News/Mopani-worms-harvested-in-KNP-20121217 (accessed 7/11/2018).

PAGES 66-67

[1] http://www.nbri.org.na/sections/economic-botany/INP/Economic-indicators (accessed 23/11/2018)

[2] Farnsworth, N.R. and Soejarto, D.D. (1988). *Global Importance of Medicinal Plants.* The Conservation of Medicinal Plants, Proceedings of an International Consultation, Chiang Mai, Thailand, Cambridge University Press.

[3] Stolton, S. and Dudley, N. (2010). *Vital Sites. The contribution of protected areas to human health*, WWF, Gland, Switzerland.

[4] Cunningham, A.B., Shanley, P. and Laird, S. (2008). Health, habitats and medicinal plant use. In: Colfer, C.J.P. (ed.) *Human health and forests: A global overview of issues, practice and policy*, Earthscan, London.

[5] James, P.B., Wardle, J., Steel, A. and Adams, J. (2018). Traditional, complementary and alternative medicine use in Sub-Saharan Africa: A systematic review. *BMJ Global Health* 3: e000895. doi:10.1136/ bmjgh-2018-000895

[6] United Nations Development Programme and National Environment Management Authority. (2017). *Biodiversity Policy and Institutional Review, National Environment Management Authority,* Kampala.

[7] Yaron, G., Mangani, R., Mlava, J., Kambewa, P., Makungwa, S., et al. (2011). *Economic Analysis of Sustainable Natural Resource Use in Malawi,* UNDP UNEP, New York and Nairobi.

[8] Yineger, H., Kelbessa, E., Bekele, T. and Lulekal, E. (2008). Plants used in traditional management of human ailments at Bale Mountains National Park, Southeastern Ethiopia, *Journal of Medicinal Plants Research* 2(6).

[9] Edwards, S.E., da Costa Rocha, I., Williamson, E.M. and Heinrich, M. (2015). *Phytopharmacy: An evidence-based guide to herbal medicinal products.* Wiley Blackwell, Chichester, UK.

[10] Mncwangi, N., Chen, W., Vermaak, I., Viljoen, A.M. and Gericke, N. (2012). Devil's claw – A review of the ethnobotany, phytochemistry and biological activity of *Harpagophytum procumbens. Journal of Ethnopharmacology* 143: 755-771.

[11] Strohbach, M. and Cole, D. (2007). Population Dynamics and Sustainable Harvesting of the Medicinal Plant *Harpagophytum procumbens* in Namibia. BfN – Skripten 203, Germany.

[12] http://www.nbri.org.na/sections/economic-botany/INP/Economic-indicators (accessed 23/11/2018).

[13] Mncwangi, N., et al. (2012). *Op cit.*

[14] https://www.worldwildlife.org/stories/devil-s-claw-an-organic-remedy-to-economic-hardship# (accessed 1/1/2019).

[15] Tilburt, J.C. and Kaptchuk, T.J. (2008). Herbal medicine research and global health: An ethical analysis. *Bulletin of the World Health Organization* 86(8): 577-656.

[16] David, B., Wolfender, J-L. and Dias, D.A. (2014). The pharmaceutical industry and natural products: historical status and new trends. *Phytochemistry Reviews.* DOI 10.1007/s11101-014-9367-z.

[17] Stolton, S. and Dudley, N. (2010). *Vital Sites. The contribution of protected areas to human health*, WWF, Gland, Switzerland.

[18] Gustafson, K.R., Munro, M.H.G., Blunt, M.H., Cardellina, M.H., McMahon, J.B., et al. (1991). HIV inhibitory natural products. 3. Diterpenes from *Homalanthus acuminatus* and *Chrysobalanus icaco. Tetrahedron* 47: 4547-4554.

[19] McGowan, J. (2006). *Out of Africa: Mysteries of Access and Benefit Sharing.* The Edmonds Institute, USA and The African Centre for Biosafety, South Africa.

[20] Peterson, M. Trophic thunder. *Berkley Science Review.* http://berkeleysciencereview.com/article/trophic-thunder/ (accessed 20/4/2019).

[21] Holding Anyonge, C., Rugalema, G., Kayambazinthu, D., Sitoe, A. and Barany, M. (2006). Fuelwood, food and medicine: The role of forests in the response to HIV and AIDS in rural areas of southern Africa. *Unasylva:* 224.

[22] Cunsolo, A. and Ellis, N. (2018). Ecological grief as a mental health response to climate change-related loss. *Nature Climate Change* 8(4): 275-281.

PAGES 68-71

[1] Balala, N. (2018). *National Wildlife Strategy.* Ministry of Tourism and Wildlife, Nairobi, Kenya.

[2] Muala, D. (2010). Tales from Gorongosa, available at http://www.gorongosa.org/sites/default/files/2010_tales_from_gorongosa_-_nearly_final_draft.pdf (accessed 25/10/2018).

[3] http://www.loewenmensch.de/lion_man.html and https://blog.britishmuseum.org/the-lion-man-an-ice-age-masterpiece/ (accessed 29/3/2019).

[4] Chauvet, J.-M., Brunel, D.E. and Hillaire, C. (1996). *Dawn of Art: The Chauvet Cave. The oldest known paintings in the world*. Harry N. Abrams, New York.

[5] Lesko, B.S. (1999). *The Great Goddesses of Egypt*. University of Oklahoma Press, Norman.

[6] http://www2.cnrs.fr/en/142.htm?debut=497 (accessed 6/11/ 2018).

[7] Black, J. and Green, A. (1992). *Gods, Demons and Symbols of Ancient Mesopotamia: An Illustrated Dictionary*. The British Museum Press, London.

[8] Mindlin, M., Geller, M.J. and Wansbrough, J.E. (eds.) (1987). *Figurative Language in the Ancient Near East*. School of Oriental and African Studies, University of London.

[9] Kideghesho, J.R. (2009). The potentials of traditional African cultural practices in mitigating overexploitation of wildlife species and habitat loss: Experience of Tanzania. *International Journal of Biodiversity Science and Management* 5(2): 83-94. DOI:10.1080/17451590903065579.

[10] Tucker, L. (2013). *Saving the White Lions: One woman's battle for Africa's most sacred animal*. North Atlantic Books, Vermont.

[11] Nyanjeka, T.M. (1996). Shona Women and the Mutupo Principle. In: Ruether, R.R. (ed.) *Women Healing Earth: Third World Women on Ecology, Feminism, and Religion*. SCM Press, London.

[12] Muala, D. (2010). *Tales from Gorongosa*, available at http://www.gorongosa.org/sites/default/files/2010_tales_from_gorongosa_-_nearly_final_draft.pdf (accessed 25/10/2018).

[13] Gebresenbet, F., Baraki, B., Yirga, G., Sillero-Zubiri, C. and Bauer, H. (2017). A culture of tolerance: Coexisting with large carnivores in the Kafa Highlands, Ethiopia. *Oryx* 52: 751-760. doi:10.1017/S0030605316001356.

[14] Hodgetts, T., Lewis, M., Bauer, H., Burnham, D., Dickman, A., et al. (2018). Improving the role of global conservation treaties in addressing contemporary threats to lions. *Biodiversity and Conservation* 27(10): 2747-2765.

[15] Hazzah, L., Bath, A., Dolreny, S., Dickman, A. and Frank, L. (2017). From attitudes to actions: Predictors of lion killing by Maasai warriors. PLOS ONE 12(1): e0170796. doi:10.1371/journal.pone.0170796.

[16] Goldman, M.J., Roque de Pinho, J. and Perry, J. (2013). Beyond ritual and economics: Maasai lion hunting and conservation politics. *Oryx* 47(4): 490-500.

[17] Hazzah, L., Dolrenry, S., Naughton, L., Edwards, C.T.T., Mwebi, O., et al. (2014). Efficacy of two lion conservation programs in Maasailand, Kenya. *Conservation Biology* 28(3): 851-860.

[18] http://lionguardians.org/ (accessed 28/3/2019).

[19] https://africanpeoplewildlife.org/warriors-wildlife/ (accessed 28/3/2019).

[20] http://www.ruahacarnivoreproject.com/lion-defenders-6/ (accessed 28/3/2019).

[21] http://ewasolions.org/conservation/warrior-watch/ (accessed 28/3/2019).

[22] http://rateltrust.org/community-wildlife-guardian/ (accessed 28/3/2019).

[23] Dolreny, S., Hazzah, L. and Frank, L.G. (2016). Conservation and monitoring of a persecuted African lion population by Maasai warriors. *Conservation Biology* 30(3): 467-475.

[24] Dickman, A., Hazzah, L., Carbone, C. and Durant, S.M. (2014). Carnivores, culture and "contagious conflict": Multiple factors influence perceived problems with carnivores in Tanzania's Ruaha landscape. *Biological Conservation* 178: 19-27.

[25] https://www.maasaiolympics.com/about-maasai-olympics-kenya (accessed 1/6/2019)

[26] Fitzherbert, E., Caro, T., Johnson, P.J., Macdonald, D.W. and Borgerhoff Mulder, E. (2014). From avengers to hunters: Leveraging collective action for the conservation of endangered lions. *Biological Conservation* 174: 84-92.

[27] Good, C., Burnham, D. and MacDonald, D.W. (2017). A cultural conscience for conservation. *Animals* 7(7): 52. doi:10.3390/ani7070052.

[28] Lindsey, P.A., Balme, G.A., Funston, P.J., Henschel, P.H. and Hunter, L.T.B. (2016). Life after Cecil: channelling global outrage into funding for conservation in Africa. *Conservation Letters* 9(4): 296-301.

PAGES 72-73

[1] McDuff, M. (2000). Thirty years of environmental education in Africa: The role of the Wildlife Clubs of Kenya. *Environmental Education Research* 6: 383-396.

[2] https://www.nationalgeographic.org/activity/lion-crittercam/ (accessed 30/12/2018).

[3] https://www.zooniverse.org/projects/zooniverse/snapshot-serengeti/classify (accessed 30/12/2018).

[4] https://instantwild.zsl.org/projects/lewa (accessed 29/3/2019).

[5] https://wildlifedirect.org/education-and-outreach/ (accessed 29/3/2019).

[6] http://ewasolions.org/conservation/lionkids/ (accessed 29/3/2019).

[7] Ministry of Tourism and Wildlife (2018). *National Wildlife Strategy 2030*, Ministry of Tourism & Wildlife, Nairobi, Kenya. Page 66.

[8] Manono, G. and Rotich, D. (2013). Seasonality effects of trends of domestic and international tourism: A case of Nairobi National Park, Kenya. *Journal of Natural Sciences Research* 3: 131-139.

[9] Okello, M.M., Kenana, L. and Kieti, D. (2012). Factors influencing domestic tourism for urban and semi-urban populations around Nairobi National Park. *Tourism Analysis* 17: 79-89.

[10] Korea National Park Service. (2009). *Korea's Protected Areas: Assessing the effectiveness of South Korea's protected areas system*, KNPS, Jeju Island and IUCN, Seoul.

PAGES 74-75

[1] Courchamp, F., Jaric, I., Albert, C., Meinard, Y., Ripple, W.J., et al. (2018). The paradoxical extinction of the most charismatic animals. *PLoS Biology* 16(4). doi.org/10.1371/ journal.pbio.2003997.

[2] https://thelionssharefund.com/ (accessed 29/4/2019).

[3] https://thelionssharefund.com/our-partners.html (accessed 29/4/2019).

[4] Bauer, H., Packer, C., Funston, P.F., Henschel, P. and Nowell, K. (2016). *Panthera leo* (errata version published in 2017). *The IUCN Red List of Threatened Species* 2016: e.T15951A115130419. http://dx.doi.org/10.2305/IUCN.UK.2016-3.RLTS.T15951A107265605.en. (accessed 30/12/2018).

PAGES 76-77

[1] https://www.washingtonpost.com/world/africa/rebels-in-the-central-african-republic-are-filling-the-void-of-an-absent-government/2018/03/25/3e11d960-2328-11e8-946c-9420060cb7bd_story.html?noredirect=on&utm_term=.4bea23c5dd74 (accessed 25/10/2018)

[2] de Merode, E., Hillman-Smith, K., Homewood, K., Pettifor, R., Rowcliffe, M. and Cowlishaw, G. (2007). The impact of armed conflict on protected areas efficacy in Central Africa. *Biology Letters* 3: 299-301.

[3] Kelly, A.B. (2015). The crumbling fortress: Territory, access, and subjectivity production in Waza National Park, Northern Cameroon. *Antipode* 47(3) : 730-747. doi: 10.1111/anti.12132.

[4] Hammil, A. (2005). Protected areas and the security community. In: McNeely, J. (ed.) *Friends for Life: New partners in support of protected areas*. IUCN, Gland, Switzerland.

[5] https://www.nrt-kenya.org/peace-and-security (accessed 29/3/2019).

[6] http://www.worldbank.org/en/country/centralafricanrepublic/overview (accessed 10/11/2018).

[7] https://www.africanparks.org/the-parks/chinko (accessed 10/11/2018).

[8] https://www.washingtonpost.com/world/africa/rebels-in-the-central-african-republic-are-filling-the-void-of-an-absent-government/2018/03/25/3e11d960-2328-11e8-946c-9420060cb7bd_story.html?noredirect=on&utm_term=.4bea23c5dd74 (accessed 10/11/2018).

[9] https://www.africanparks.org/the-parks/chinko (accessed 10/11/2018).

[10] https://blog.nationalgeographic.org/2017/03/09/heart-of-africa-expedition-positions-for-final-trek-lions-observed-from-ultralite/ (accessed 10/11/2018).

[11] Kelly, A.B. (2015). *Op cit.*

[12] Kelly Pennaz, A., Ahmadou, M., Moritz, M. and Scholte, P. (2018). Not seeing the cattle for the elephants: The implications of discursive linkages between Boko Haram and wildlife poaching in Waza National Park, Cameroon. *Conservation and Society* 16(2): 125-135.

[13] Fobuzie, P.T. and de Longh, H. (2017). Report on conservation of the lion population in Waza NP, Northern Cameroon: An assessment of the status of lions and other wildlife. Centre for Environment and Development Studies in Cameroon / Leo Foundation. (cited on http://lionalert.org/alert/lions_in/Cameroon, accessed 10/11/2018).

[14] Neme, L. (2014). For rangers in the front lines of anti-poaching wars, daily trauma. *National Geographic* June 27 2014.

[15] Hillman-Smith, K. (2018). Wildlife and warfare: A case study of pachyderms in Garamba National Park, DRC. *Pachyderm* 59.

[16] Braack, L., Sandwith, T., Peddle, D. and Petermann, T. (2006). *Security Considerations in the Planning and Management of Transboundary Conservation Areas.* IUCN, Gland, Switzerland and Cambridge, UK.

PAGES 78-81

[1] African Development Bank Group. (2014). *Payment for Environmental Services. A promising tool for Natural Resources Management in Africa.* African Development Bank Group, Abidjan, Côte d'Ivoire.

[2] Peter Lindsey interview: http://www.theeastafrican.co.ke/business/Protect-Africa-lions/2560-4127986-2d49uc/index.html (accessed 9/10/2018).

[3] Bughin, J., Chironga, M., Desvaux, G., Ermias, T., Jacobson, P., et al. (2016). *Lions on The Move II: Realizing the Potential of Africa's Economies. Executive Summary.* McKinsey Global Institute.

[4] Satterthwaite, D. (2014). Cities of more than 500,000 people, Visualisation. International Institute for Environment and Development, London. http://www.iied.org/cities-interactive-data-visual (accessed 1/11/2018).

[5] Humphrey, S. (2012). *Africa's Ecological Footprint.* WWF and ADB.

[6] Angel, S., Parent, J., Civco, D.L. and Blei, A.M. (2011). *Making Room for a Planet of Cities.* Lincoln Institute of Land Policy, Cambridge, MA.

[7] African Development Bank Group. (2018). *Africa Prospects. Vol 1.* African Development Bank Group, Abidjan, Côte d'Ivoire.

[8] Ibid

[9] Laurance, W.F. and Burgués Arrea, I. (2017). Roads to riches or ruin? *Science* 358(6362): 442-444.

[10] AfDB and WWF (2015). *African Ecological Futures. 2015.* WWF, Nairobi.

[11] Watkins, M.H. and Griffith, C.A. (eds.). (2015). *Synthesis Report from the 2nd International Conference on Urbanization and Global Environmental Change. Urban Transitions & Transformations: Science, Synthesis and Policy.* Urbanization and Global Environmental Change Project, Tempe, USA.

[12] UNICEF and World Health Organisation. (2015). *Progress on Sanitation and Drinking Water – 2015 update and MDG assessment.* Geneva.

[13] Zingore, S., Mutegi, J., Agesa, B., Tamene, L. and Kihara, J. (2015). Soil degradation in sub-Saharan Africa and crop production options for soil rehabilitation. *Better Crops* 99(1): 24-26.

[14] The World Bank Group. (2012). *State of the Clean Energy Sector in Sub-Saharan Africa.* Washington, DC.

[15] Hodgetts, T., Lewis, M., Bauer, H., Burnham, D., Dickman, A., et al. (2018). Improving the role of global conservation treaties in addressing contemporary threats to lions. *Biodiversity and Conservation* 27(10): 2747-2765.

[16] https://www.afdb.org/en/news-and-events/the-2018-mid-term-review-of-the-african-development-fund-kigali-rwanda-18598/ (accessed 25/10/2018).

[17] Ministry of Tourism and Wildlife. (2018). *National Wildlife Strategy 2030*, Ministry of Tourism & Wildlife, Nairobi, Kenya.

[18] http://revealingbenin.com/ (accessed 10/11/2018).

PAGES 82-83

[1] Dr Cristiana Pasca Palmer, UN Assistant Secretary General and Executive Secretary of the Convention on Biological Diversity, Senior level briefing on biodiversity finance, 6th August 2018, Namibia, https://resmob.org/wp-content/uploads/2018/09/Dr.-Palmer-Keynote-Remarks_Biodiversity-Economy.pdf (accessed 29/12/2018).

[2] Costanza, R., de Groot, R., Braat, L., Kubiszewski, I., Fioramonti, L., Sutton, P., et al. (2017). Twenty years of ecosystem services: How far have we come and how far do we still need to go? Ecosystem Services 28: 1-16.

[3] Scholte, S.S.K., van Teeffelen, A.J.A. and Verburg, P.J. (2015). Integrating socio-cultural perspectives into ecosystem service valuation: A review of concepts and methods. Ecological Economics 114: 67-78.

[4] Costanza, R., de Groot, R., Sutton, P., van der Ploeg, S., Anderson, S.J., et al. (2014). Changes in the global value of ecosystem services. Global Environmental Change 26: 152-158.

[5] de Groot, R., Brander, L., Ploeg, S., Costanza, R., Bernard, F., et al. (2012). Global estimates of the value of ecosystems and their services in monetary units. Ecosystem Services 1: 50-61.

[6] Costanza, R., et al. (2017). *Op cit.*

PAGES 84-87

[1] Lindsey, P.A., Miller, J.R.B., Petracca, L.S., Coad, L., Dickman, A.J., Fitzgerald, K.H., et al. (2018). More than $1 billion needed annually to secure Africa's protected areas with lions. *Proceedings of the National Academy of Sciences* 115: 45. https://doi.org/10.1073/pnas.1805048115.

[2] https://www.moodiedavittreport.com/world-number-one-incheon-airport-posts-record-duty-free-sales-of-us2-4-billion-in-2018/ (accessed 1/6/2019)

[3] Lindsey, P.A., et al. (2018). *Op cit.*

[4] https://kwcakenya.com/download/conservancy-leaders-conference-report-2018/?wpdmdl=11369 (accessed 5/4/2019).

[5] Dickman, A.J., Macdonald, E.A. and Macdonald, D.W. (2011). A review of financial instruments to pay for predator conservation and encourage human–carnivore coexistence. *PNAS* 108: 49.

[6] Anyango-Van Zwieten, N., Van Der Duim, R. and Visseren-Hamakers, I. (2015). Compensating for livestock killed by lions: Payment for environmental services as a policy arrangement. *Environmental Conservation*, 42(4): 363-372. doi:10.1017/S0376892915000090.

[7] Dickman, A.J., et al. (2011). *Op cit.*

[8] Parker, C., Cranford, M., Oakes, N. and Leggett, M. (ed.). (2012). *The Little Biodiversity Finance Book*, Global Canopy Programme, Oxford.

[9] Spenceley, A., Rylance, A. and Laiser, S.L. (2017). Protected area entrance fees in Tanzania: The search for competitiveness and value for money. *Koedoe* 59(1): a1442. https://doi. org/10.4102/koedoe. v59i1.1442.

[10] www.greenclimate.fund (accessed 29/4/2019).

[11] Parker, C., et al. (2012). *Op cit.*

[12] USAID. (2018). *Experiences and lessons learned in payments for ecosystem services (PES) in East Africa,* Tetra Tech, USA and Land Trees and Sustainability Africa (LTSA), Nairobi.

[13] https://www.africanparks.org/the-parks/chinko (accessed 10/11/2018).

[14] Parker, C., et al. (2012). *Op cit.*

[15] Cumming, T.L., Shackleton, R.T., Förster, J., Dini, J., Khan, A., Gumula, M., et al. (2017). Achieving the national development agenda and the Sustainable Development Goals (SDGs) through investment in ecological infrastructure: A case study of South Africa. *Ecosystem Services,* 27 (Part B): 253-260. http://dx.doi.org/10.1016/j.ecoser.2017.05.005.

[16] Parker, C., et al. (2012). *Op cit.*

[17] Oates, N. and Marani, M. (2017). *Making water infrastructure investment decisions in a changing climate. A political economy study of river basin development in Kenya,* Overseas Development Institute, London, UK.

[18] Cumming, T.L., *et al.* (2017). *Op cit.*

[19] Yaron, G., Mangani, R., Mlava, J., Kambewa, P., Makungwa, S., Mtethiwa, A., et al. (2011). *Economic Analysis of Sustainable Natural Resource Use in Malawi.* Ministry of Development Planning and Cooperation, UNEP and UNDP, Malawi, figures updated to take into consideration inflation between 2007 and 2019 using https://www.officialdata.org/us/inflation/2007?amount=5 (accessed 14/1/2019).

[20] Valentini, R., Arneth, A., Bombelli, A., Castaldi, S., Cazzolla Gatti, R., et al. (2014). A full greenhouse gases budget of Africa: Synthesis, uncertainties, and vulnerabilities. *Biogeosciences* 11: 381-407. doi:10.5194/bg-11-381-2014

PAGES 88-89

[1] https://www.nationalgeographic.org/newsroom/national-geographic-joins-forces-with-african-parks-the-wyss-foundation-and-the-republic-of-benin-to-protect-critical-west-african-ecosystem (accessed 15/10/2018).

[2] http://revealingbenin.com/en/why-benin/#revealing-benin (accessed 10/11/2018).

[3] Sogbohossou, E.A., Bauer, H., Loveridge, A., Funston, P.J., De Snoo, G.R., Sinsin, B. and De Iongh, H.D. (2014). Social Structure of Lions *(Panthera leo)* is Affected by Management in Pendjari Biosphere Reserve, Benin. *PLoS ONE* 9(1): e84674.

[4] http://revealingbenin.com/en/2018/02/01/pendjari/ (accessed 10/11/2018).

[5] http://revealingbenin.com/en/projects/pendjari/ (accessed 10/11/2018).

Find out more about The New Lion Economy at:
https://youtu.be/cuKlsQaHP6U